Measuring

impact

MATHS HOMEWORK

Published by Scholastic Publications Ltd,
Villiers House,
Clarendon Avenue,
Leamington Spa,
Warwickshire CV32 5PR

© 1994 Scholastic Publications Ltd

Reprinted 1994

UNIVERSITY OF
NORTH LONDON

Activities by the IMPACT Project
at the University of North London,
collated and rewritten by Ruth
Merttens and Ros Leather

Editor Noel Pritchard
Assistant editor Sophie Jowett
Designer Tracey Ramsey
Series designer Anna Oliwa
Illustrations Lucinda Williams, ArtQuirks
Cover illustration Roger Wade Walker

Designed using Aldus Pagemaker
Processed by Salvo Print and Design
Artwork by David Harban Design, Warwick
Printed in Great Britain
by Clays Ltd, St Ives plc

British Library Cataloguing-in-Publication Data
A catalogue record for this book is
available from the British Library.

ISBN 0-590-53156-5

Measuring

impact
CONTENTS

Measuring

impact CONTENTS

impact
INTRODUCTION

This series of IMPACT books is designed to help you run a non-traditional homework scheme. Through the use of take-home maths activities, children can share maths with a parent/carer in the context of the home. The results of these activities then feed back into the classwork at school.

IMPACT works through the following processes:
● Teachers plan their maths for the next few weeks as usual and consider which parts might usefully be done at home.
● Teachers look through selected activities which fit in with what they are planning.
● The activities are photocopied and sent home with the children every week or fortnight.
● The results of each activity are brought back into the classroom by the children and form part of the following week's classwork.

In practice this process will be slightly different in each classroom and in each school. Teachers may adapt it to fit their own way of working and the ethos of the school in which they work. Most schools send out IMPACT activities fortnightly, although some do send it weekly. There is some evidence to suggest that weekly activities get a slightly better response and help to raise standards more effectively than fortnightly, but this is not conclusive. The important point is that each teacher should feel comfortable with how often the IMPACT activities are used in his/her class.

Planning

When you, the teacher, are looking at your work and deciding what maths, roughly speaking, you plan to be doing over the next few weeks, all that is necessary is to consider which parts may usefully be done or practised at home. It is helpful if, over a period of time, a variety of activities are chosen. These tend to fall into three broad categories:
● Activities which practise a skill – these are useful in that they can be followed up in the routine classwork the children are doing. They must be carefully selected by the teacher according to the level of the children.
● Activities which collect data – these lead into work on data-handling and representation.
● Activities in which children measure or make something – this produces an object or some measurements to be used later in class.

The activities in this book are divided into sections under the maths topic headings: length, area, weight, volume and capacity, money, time and temperature. Teachers' notes relating to the individual activities are featured on pages six to ten. A page of squared paper is included on page 127 and can be photocopied to accompany activities as required. Links to National Curriculum attainment targets are included in the teachers' notes and numerals in brackets refer to the programmes of study, so AT 2/1 (iii, iv) refers to Attainment Target 2, Level 1, Programmes of Study 3 and 4. Details of how these relate to the curricula in Scotland and Northern Ireland are given on page 128.

Working with parents

It is important for the success of IMPACT that the activities taken home are seen by the parents to be maths. We always suggest, at least until IMPACT is up and running and parents' confidence in it is well established, that activities are chosen which have a clearly mathematical purpose. Save the more 'wacky' activities until later! You will get a much better response if parents believe that what they are doing is maths.

Each activity contains a note to parents which explains the purpose of the activity and how they can best help. It also gives a reference to National Curriculum attainment targets – although not to any level. Teachers who prefer not to have these can white them out. The IMPACT activities should be accompanied by an IMPACT diary, enabling parents and children to make their comments. See page 128 for details.

Making the most of IMPACT

The quickest way to reduce the number of children who share the maths at home is to ignore or be negative about the work they bring back into school. When the children come running into the classroom, tripping over the string which went twice round their cat, it is difficult to welcome them all individually but it is crucial that the activities done at home are followed up in classwork. The nature and type of this follow-up work depends very much upon the nature of the activity, and specific suggestions are made in the teachers' notes. However, some general points apply:
● Number activities, such as games, can often be repeated in a more formalised way in the classwork. For example, if the children have been playing a dice game, throwing two dice and adding the totals, they can continue to do this in the classroom, but this time they can record all the 'sums' in their maths book. This applies to any skills-practice activity.
● Data-collecting activities, of any description, need to be followed up by allowing the children to work together in small groups to collate, analyse and represent their joint data. This will inevitably involve children in a discussion as to how their data was obtained, and any problems they encountered while obtaining it.
● If the children have made or measured something at home, the information or the object needs to be used as part of the resulting classwork. This will not be too difficult since this type of activity is selected by the teacher precisely in order to provide the measurements or shapes for use in class.

The implication of this is that it is wise to select a variety of activities to send home. No teacher wants to drown in data, nor do they want all the IMPACT activities to result in more routine number work. Some activities generate lots of follow-up work while others simply require minimal follow-up – perhaps just a discussion about who won and who lost, and how many times people played the game.

Many of the activities can lead to an attractive display or enable the teacher to make a class book. Such a book does not have to be 'grand'. It can be simply five or six large sheets of sugar paper folded in the middle and stitched/stapled with the children's work mounted inside it. The children love these books, and they make a fine record of their work. An IMPACT display board in the school entrance hall gives parents a sense that their work at home is appreciated.

For further details of IMPACT see page 128.

Teachers' Notes

LENGTH

Take three bottles This is an ideal activity for comparing heights and is more interesting if you use a variety of bottles. Children could order them by height. Discuss how many bottles are taller than the shampoo bottle and so on. They could use bricks to measure bottle heights. Using no more than three bottles can the children estimate which will hold the most water? How do they know? Will it be the same for sand as for water?
National Curriculum: AT 1/1 (i); AT 4/1 (iii, v)

Find three toys Children could cut out their toys and work in pairs to order six toys. They could estimate the length of their pictures, then measure them using non-standard units. Toy pictures and measuring apparatus could be recorded into a class book.
National Curriculum: AT 1/1 (i); AT 4/1 (iii, v)

Find five leaves Children could work in pairs to cut out their leaves and reorder them to stick into a class book. Ask questions such as: How many leaves are larger than the yellow leaf?
National Curriculum: AT 1/1 (i, ii); AT 4/1 (v)

Three shoes Children could cut out outlines of their shoes and work in pairs to order their six shoes. They could estimate and measure the widths of their shoes using non-standard units then make a class display around a big shoe, for example 'There Was an Old Woman Who Lived in a Shoe'.
National Curriculum: AT 1/1 (i); AT 4/1 (iii, v)

Teddy's headband Children could work in groups and order themselves by headband length. Groups could combine until you have a class teddy headband order. How many teddies have headbands longer/shorter than a ruler? Ask children to stand up if their teddy's headband is shorter than 'this piece of string'. How many teddies are left?
National Curriculum: AT 1/1 (i, ii); AT 4/1 (v)

Daisy chains This activity could be extended in class. Children could see how many of their chains are needed to make half a metre. Are there any chains that are exactly 20cm? How many are longer/shorter?
National Curriculum: AT 1/1 (i,ii); AT 4/1 (iii, v)

Long or wide? Children could order the class/families by height and width separately, using their strips of paper. Each child could write their own label indicating their comparative position. Are both orders the same?
National Curriculum: AT 1/1 (i, ii); AT 4/1 (iii, v)

Me and my helper Discuss with the children how many times each of them 'fitted' into their partner's height. Was it usually about the same? (It is usually about twice.) Discuss how adults are different heights. You could make a height chart on the wall dividing the children into three bands – below a red line, above a blue line or between the two (the red line is at about 1.1m, the blue line at about 1.25m). These could be varied according to the size of the children in your class.
National Curriculum: AT 1/1 (i, ii); AT 2/2 (vii)

Am I square? Children can sort all the objects in their lines into different sets, e.g. books, comics, pencils, spoons, etc. How can they sort the different sets – metal objects, paper objects and so on? The children can also work in pairs to make a line of Multilink or Unifix as long as themselves. Can they count how many bricks there are?
National Curriculum: AT 1/1 (i, ii); AT 4/1 (iii)

How tall is teddy? You will need a supply of different-sized leaves for the children to draw round. They could make a family of three bears and measure them with large, medium and small leaves. Which sized leaves are the best for measuring? How many more big leaves are needed for Daddy bear than for Mummy bear? The bears brought from home could be discussed and displayed alongside the bear family.
National Curriculum: AT 1/2 (i, ii); AT 2/2 (vii)

How fat is teddy? Children could arrange their strips of paper in order of length. These could be individually curved into circles. How many of the circles are bigger than a saucer? Ask the children if their teddy was taller or shorter than his waist measurement.
National Curriculum: AT 1/2 (i, ii); AT 2/2 (vii)

Find a plate Plate outlines could be ordered by size. Children may like to cut strips to show circumferences and decorate them with handspan prints. These could be hung on a washing line with questions such as: How many plates with a circumference of more than four handspan prints are there?
National Curriculum: AT 1/2 (i, ii); AT 2/2 (vii)

Book perimeters Children could make handspan chains to show their book perimeters. These could be ordered. How many handspans difference are there between the biggest and the smallest book? The hands could be decorated, numbered and displayed in order.
National Curriculum: AT 1/2 (i, ii); AT 2/2 (vii)

IMPACT perimeters Children could use their handspan to estimate and measure various objects in school. You could make a handspan chain (five or ten single handspans) to use in estimating and measuring larger lengths.
National Curriculum: AT 1/2 (i, ii); AT 2/2 (vii)

The fattest bottle Look at a selection of bottles in school. Children could work in groups to investigate and measure the bottles: tallest, fattest, heaviest, holds most/least and so on.
National Curriculum: AT 1/2 (i, ii); AT 2/2 (viii)

Hopping Children could discuss whether their competition at home was fair. Can they decide on the rules for a fair competition? The new class measurements could then be recorded as strips, ordered and then hung up on a washing line. Differences could be calculated using non-standard or standard units. The work could go into a class book containing the children's written explanations.
National Curriculum: AT 1/2 (i, ii); AT 2/2 (vii, viii)

Decimetre measure Children could stick their work into a class book with answers to questions such as: How much taller is the tallest person than the shortest person in your family? How much taller is the tallest person than you?
National Curriculum: AT 1/2 (i, ii); AT 2/2 (viii)

Exactly 20 centimetres Decorate the 20cm strips and join them together to make metre strips. These could be used to measure objects in the classroom. Ask the children for estimates before the metre strips are used.
National Curriculum: AT 1/2 (i, ii); AT 2/2 (viii)

Quarter my height Children could order then measure their strips using a variety of non-standard and standard units. Which units were the most appropriate for measuring these strips?
National Curriculum: AT 1/2 (i, ii); AT 2/2 (vi)

Race to one metre In class children could work in pairs using place value counting apparatus to make their own heights. Each child could use coloured strips to make their height and these could be ordered and displayed. They may like to draw their face to place on their strip.
National Curriculum: AT 1/2 (i, ii); AT 2/2 (ii, viii)

Hands along the window Working in groups the children can create a block graph according to how many of their hands fitted along their window. Ask them to help you put all the results on one class graph. What can they see from the classroom window? Draw this. Make a display or class book of their drawings.
National Curriculum: AT 1/2 (i, ii); AT 2/2 (vii)

Shared metre daisy chain What about a daisy-chain making competition working in pairs? Who can make the longest daisy chain in five minutes? How many are longer than a metre? How many metres long are all the chains put together? How many children will fit along the chain?
National Curriculum: AT 1/2 (i, ii); AT 2/2 (viii)

A new leaf Children could be grouped and each group could choose a different criterion for sorting their leaves (length, area, time taken). The information could be recorded and displayed with their leaves in a class book.
National Curriculum: AT 1/2 (i, ii); AT 2/2 (viii)

Around the table Ask the children to make perimeter strips for different tables. These could be ordered and various problems discussed. Are all the tables with the same perimeter the same shape? How many rectangular shapes can be made with this length? Which shape would you choose? Why? The various table shapes could be made from paper with the lengths, widths and perimeters displayed. Children could write captions to say why some shapes were more suitable than others.
National Curriculum: AT 1/2 (i, ii); AT 2/2 (viii)

Book measures The children can compare string lengths, perhaps using Multilink or Unifix. They can measure round big books in school. What is the largest perimeter they can find?
National Curriculum: AT 1/2 (i, ii); AT 2/2 (vii)

Measure a box Children could work in small groups and choose a criterion for sorting their boxes. Other groups could then try to establish which criterion has been chosen for sorting.
National Curriculum: AT 1/2 (i, ii); AT 2/2 (viii)

Measure your shoe Children could work in groups to collect the various pieces of information. This could be displayed in a class book for all to share.
National Curriculum: AT 1/2 (i, ii); AT 2/2 (viii)

Turning a wheel This activity will provide plenty of opportunity to discuss why wheels are different-sizes. Discuss the word circumference. Children could work in small groups to compare and order their wheel measurements. These could then be decorated and displayed.
National Curriculum: AT 1/2 (i, ii, iii); AT 2/2 (vii, viii)

Diameter and circumference Discuss any conclusions the children have reached. They could arrange their circles and strips in order and hang them on a washing line.
National Curriculum: AT 1/2 (ii, iii); AT 2/2 (viii)

Framing a picture Children could set up a framing shop. You will need a selection of pictures and a variety of coloured strips to use for framing. They may like to advertise and design a notice for the price of the frames.
National Curriculum: AT 1/2 (i, ii); AT 2/2 (iii, v, viii); AT 2/3 (iii)

Lace borders A supply of cotton squares and cheap lace could form the basis for a class shop. Children could choose fabric and lace to buy and actually make presents for Mother's Day, birthdays, school fêtes, etc.
National Curriculum: AT 1/2 (i, ii); AT 2/2 (iii, v, viii); AT 2/3 (iii)

Which colours are easiest to see? Children may like to design a number line using a black/white background with each number a different colour. Which numbers are the easiest/most difficult to see? Use your number line for counting activities.
National Curriculum: AT 1/2 (i, ii); AT 2/2 (vii)

AREA

Does it fit? Children's foot drawings can be used as the basis for a great deal of comparative work – both in length and area. Which foot is the longest? Which is the shortest? Can they cover their foot with small bricks (Centicubes)? How many does it take? Make a graph of the number of bricks used to cover each foot. Children can work out how many of their feet fit along a table, or up the door and so on.
National Curriculum: AT 1/2 (i); AT 2/2 (vii, viii)

Square foot Children can cut round and decorate their 'feet' back in class. They can compare the areas of their feet with each other, and display these in sets categorised according to area – all the feet of roughly the same area in individual sets.
National Curriculum: AT 1/2 (i, ii); AT 2/2 (vii, viii)

Tin areas Children can compare their findings. Did they all get the same answer? If not, why not? This should lead to a discussion about standard units. Why are tins not a very good way of measuring area? Do circles tessellate? The children can then start to calculate the area of their piece of paper using things other than tins, for example matchboxes, small square templates and so on.
National Curriculum: AT 1/2 (i, ii, iii); AT 2/2 (vii, viii)

Toy areas Children can talk about their toys and sort them into sets based on the size of the area their toy covered. Drawings of the toys can be arranged in order of area from smallest to largest to make a class book or a display.
National Curriculum: AT 1/2 (i, ii); AT 2/2 (vii, viii)

Square metres You will have a lot of square metres(!), but these can be used to show children that it takes quite a lot of things to cover them. They can try covering them with books, with large bricks, or with anything else in the classroom which is an appropriate size. Check that their square metres are all the same size and talk about the need for a standard unit.
National Curriculum: AT 1/2 (i, ii, iii); AT 2/2 (vii, viii)

Dinosaur tiles Children can share their drawings and discuss how large their chosen object was. They can use their dinosaur tiles to measure things in the classroom. Can they measure by counting the number of rows of tiles? Finally, they can make a nice wall display of the dinosaur tiles!

National Curriculum: AT 1/2 (i, ii); AT 2/2 (vii, viii)

Book at bedtime Children can talk about the different areas of their beds. Discuss the different sizes of their books and the need for a standard unit. Can they measure their book using a square decimetre or another convenient-sized unit? They can draw their book and write its area next to it for display.
National Curriculum: AT 1/2 (i, ii, iii); AT 2/2 (vii, viii)

Area count up Children can compare their book areas – and also their book scores! Did the books with the largest areas score the highest? They can cut out the drawings of their books and place them in order along the wall, according to their area. Can they think of other things they can use to measure the area of their books?
National Curriculum: AT 1/2 (i, ii); AT 2/2 (vii, viii)

Best rooms Children can calculate the area of the room they have chosen. Any who did not manage to do the activity at home can, of course, draw the classroom. There will be some discussion about the size of a pace. Try this out in class. What might they have used instead of a pace? They can also work out the area of each other's plans.
National Curriculum: AT 1/2 (i, ii, iii); AT 2/2 (vii)

New areas This activity leads into lots of work on the conservation of area. Children can cut out their shapes and mount them for display in sorted sets. Can they design a set of shapes which all have an area of 24 squares? How many rectangles can they make which all have an area of 24?
National Curriculum: AT 1/2 (i, ii); AT 2/2 (vii)

Head areas Children can paint their head shapes in a checked pattern using the unit squares. How large are their heads? Display them in sets on the wall according to the area they cover. It is important to discuss the need for a standard unit and the fact that the usual standard unit square is 1cm squared.

National Curriculum: AT 1/2 (i, ii); AT 2/2 (vii, viii)

Coin areas Discuss what the children found out. Did they correctly estimate the areas? Which coin had the largest area? Do the coins take up more space in your pocket if they have a larger area? How many of the small 5p coins might cover the same number of squares as the 50p?
National Curriculum: AT 1/2 (i, ii, iii); AT 2/2 (vii)

Flat fruits Cut out and mount the children's drawings of fruit. Can they sort them into sets according to area? You will need to discuss which ones covered the most squares, and which ones covered the least. This is good practice in ordering and in teaching that we can measure in two dimensions. However, it is not necessary to introduce the term 'area' yet if you do not want to.
National Curriculum: AT 1/1 (i, ii); AT 2/2 (vii)

Fitting together Children can discuss which shapes tessellated and which did not. They can be encouraged to invent their own patterns using the tessellating shapes. Do some of those which do not tessellate leave interesting-shaped gaps between them?
National Curriculum: AT 1/1 (ii, iii)

T-shirt cover up Children can share their work, looking at and discussing all the things they found to cover their T-shirts. Using the notion of *covering*, they can be encouraged to cover a book, using bricks or cards, and then to count how many they have used. Their T-shirts may be good enough to display!
National Curriculum: AT 1/1 (i, ii)

VOLUME AND CAPACITY

Drink up Talk about the different containers that we use and discuss the notions of empty and full, half-empty, etc. The children can draw what they had to drink and sort their drawings into sets according to the type of container.
National Curriculum: AT 1/1 (i, ii)

Making containers Children can compare the different containers they bring in. You may be able to fill some of them with lentils or rice and discuss which ones hold the most. The different containers can be used to make a fine display.
National Curriculum: AT 1/1 (i, ii)

Balloon capacity NB This activity is very successful but it really works only if you provide a balloon for each child to take home! Back in class, the children can compare the capacities of their balloons. They can make a block graph showing how many balloons held which amounts. What was the usual amount? What was the least?
National Curriculum: AT 1/2 (i, ii); AT 2/2 (vii)

Up to the brim Compare saucepans as the children describe how many cupfuls they used. Make a graph or a pictogram using small saucepans! Plot the capacity – four cups or five cups and so on – against the number of saucepans holding that amount.
National Curriculum: AT 1/2 (i, ii, iii); AT 2/2 (vii)

L-driver Having a variety of different litre containers to hand in the classroom means that it is easy to demonstrate the difference between the shape of a container and its capacity. Fill up as many of the containers as you can so that they are half-full. What does half a litre look like in the different shaped containers? How about a quarter of a litre?
National Curriculum: AT 1/2 (i, ii); AT 2/2 (vii, viii)

Handy overspill Working in groups, the children can compare their results. How do they account for the differences? They can all draw around their hands, colour them in, and then order them on a display in the order of the volumes measured in spoonfuls.
National Curriculum: AT 1/2 (i, ii); AT 2/2 (vii)

Toy volumes Use all the children's drawings to generate discussion of size in relation to volume. Are the tallest or longest things always the largest? It is important to develop an idea of the volume of a solid as the

amount of space it takes up. Children can choose one of their toys – their favourite – and draw it carefully to go in a set with other toys of similar volume. Display the sets.
National Curriculum: AT 1/1 (i, ii); AT 2/2 (vii)

Comparing cups Children can discuss the relative sizes of their containers. Perhaps they can make a graph or chart of the different-sized mugs/cups. Discuss the need for an appropriate unit. Was a tablespoon the right size, or can they suggest something better? This may lead on to discussion of the need for a standard unit.
National Curriculum: AT 1/2 (i, ii, iii); AT 2/2 (vii, viii)

Value for money? This activity leads into a discussion about the different units that we can use to measure volume or capacity. The children can talk about the relative sizes of the different containers that they studied. It is helpful if they can follow this up by handling a litre container and talking about millilitres and cubic centimetres (i.e. that 1ml = 1cc). A medicine spoon is a good example of 5ml.
National Curriculum: AT 1/2 (i, ii); AT 2/2 (vii, viii)

Cut it open Children can share each other's opened out boxes and discuss the shapes they can see. This activity should enable the children to make a net for themselves and fold it up to make a solid.
National Curriculum: AT 1/2 (i, ii, iii); AT 4/2 (i)

Fold it up The children's boxes should form the basis for both a lovely display and some interesting work. Discuss how many faces, how many edges and how many corners they have, then talk about how big they are. How many millilitres do they hold? Use a medicine spoon to measure their volume – make sure that the children guess first!
National Curriculum: AT 1/2 (i, ii); AT 4/2 (i)

Fair share Children can cut out their drawings of mugs and compare the figures for their capacities. They can order the mugs in terms of their size and discuss whether

tablespoons are a suitable unit to use for measuring them. Perhaps they could create a graph of the different numbers of mugs of different capacities.
National Curriculum: AT 1/2 (i, ii, iii); AT 2/2 (vii)

Spilling fun Children can share their drawings and talk about who was right and who was wrong. It is a good exercise to have several containers that you have brought in where it is not at all clear which is the larger, and then to allow small groups of children to work together to find out. If they want to compare more than two, and to put them in order, they will have to devise ways of doing this.
National Curriculum: AT 1/2 (i, ii, iii); AT 2/2 (vii)

Bubble sort Children will all have stories to tell about who was right and who was wrong about the relative size of their containers. They can mount their drawings into a class book or display with all the people who were completely right on one page, all those who only got one wrong on another, and so on. It is a useful exercise to allow them to do a similar bubble sort in class, using a different set of containers.
National Curriculum: AT 1/2 (i, ii, iii); AT 2/2 (vii)

Unit hunt Children can share their results and, working in groups, can collect up all the things that are measured using a particular unit, for example in grams. They can then collate these findings on to a chart under the various measures headings – weight, capacity, length, area, time, etc. Which were left off their lists? Talk about the ways in which different standard units are used – both in terms of their appropriateness and historically and culturally.
National Curriculum: AT 1/2 (i, ii, iii); AT 2/2 (viii)

WEIGHT

Are they the same? This activity will generate a lot of discussion about size and

weight. Encourage the children to sort the things they have found into sets according to how heavy they are – all those heavier than a child/all those things heavier than 2kg/all those things lighter than 2kg and heavier than 1kg/all those lighter than 1kg and so on. The sets can be displayed on the wall.
National Curriculum: AT 1/1 (ii, iii); AT 2/2 (viii)

Heavy weights When children bring their drawings back into school, either paste them into a class book or make a display. Encourage them to categorise the things – which are larger than them, which are smaller? What are the things made of – metal, wood, plastic and so on? What sorts of things are heavy, and what materials are light? This will lead into comparing objects in class.
National Curriculum: AT 1/1 (ii, iii)

Weight watch out Children can sort their drawings according to the unit of weight used. Probably most will be grams but some may be pounds or ounces. Some may not be units of weight but of volume and this will need to be discussed. Sort the drawings according to how heavy they are, putting all those of a similar weight in the same set.
National Curriculum: AT 1/2 (i, ii); AT 2/2 (vii, viii)

More or less Children can discuss the different items they found. Working in groups, they can then sort all their foods into sets according to weight, for example they may have a set of things weighing 375 grams. (The sets may need to be approximate.) They can then work out how much all the things in each set would weigh together. Which set is the heaviest? Does it have the most things in it?
National Curriculum: AT 1/2 (i, ii); AT 2/2 (vii, viii)

Toy weights Children can work in groups and make a giant list, putting all their toys in order according to their weight. Perhaps they can each draw one of their favourite toys, and then you can make a display of these drawings in order of weight with their weights in units written underneath.

National Curriculum: AT 1/2 (i, ii); AT 2/2 (vii, viii)

Wait for the weight Children can play this game in class using Multilink or bricks. The numbers can be made slightly larger and the bricks can be compared on a balance. It is useful to talk about weighing on scales as well since many of the children will have done this at home.
National Curriculum: AT 1/2 (i); AT 2/2 (vii, viii)

MONEY

Which coin? Play a game using a 'feely bag'. Put one coin of every value in the bag. Children then take turns to try to identify the coin that they are feeling before taking it out. You may like to discuss the value of this game – being able to identify coins in the dark or if a person is blind.
National Curriculum: AT 1/1 (i, ii); AT 2/1 (i); AT 5/1 (i, ii)

Coin routes Ask the children to sit in a circle and place a selection of coins in the middle. All children except one turn round and this child describes a coin without naming it. The other children turn round and take turns at trying to identify the coin from the description.
National Curriculum: AT 1/1 (i, ii); AT 2/2 (v); AT 5/2 (iv)

Collection Children could sort the coins into different sets using a variety of criteria: colour, shape, value, size and so on.
National Curriculum: AT 1/1 (i, ii); AT 2/2 (v); AT 5/1 (i, ii)

Most and least This activity is ideal for the children when using a class shop in role-play activities.
National Curriculum: AT 1/1 (i, ii); AT 2/1 (i)

Coin line-up Children could make a simple shop using everyday classroom objects and price them to exact coin values. Other groups could record the articles and prices. These could be changed frequently to give all children an opportunity to price objects.
National Curriculum: AT 1/2 (i, ii); AT 2/2 (v)

Charting money Children could work in pairs to find out how the totals have been made, for example draw the coins needed to make 20p in 5ps.
National Curriculum: AT 1/2 (i, ii, iii); AT 2/2 (v); AT 5/2 (i, ii)

Venn money Children could work in pairs to record their sets as a pictogram. They will need to think of different criteria for their work: colour, shape, value, weight.
National Curriculum: AT 1/2 (i, ii, iii); AT 2/2 (v); AT 5/2 (iv)

Window shopping Children could work in pairs to find three ways of making the value of their article. Does one of the ways show the least number of coins possible to make this total?
National Curriculum: AT 1/2 (i, ii); AT 2/2 (v)

Big money Children could price articles in the class shop and use their notes as pretend big value notes.
National Curriculum: AT 1/2 (i, ii); AT 2/2 (v)

Coin toss up Small groups of children could play an extension of this game during spare moments. A small handful of coins are shaken and put in a central area. The coins are then sorted into heads and tails sets. Which set is worth more?
National Curriculum: AT 1/2 (i, ii, iii); AT 2/2 (iii, v)

Handy coins Children could arrange their hands in value order, and ask questions such as: How many hands are worth exactly 20p? How many hands are worth less than 10p? Hands could be displayed on a washing line with the totals recorded on the hands.
National Curriculum: AT 1/2 (i, ii, iii); AT 2/2 (iii, v)

Price tags Children could arrange their groceries in price order and work out various additions using money, for example the price of dairy products. Who has the most/least expensive dairy products? Why do prices vary?
National Curriculum: AT 1/2 (ii, iii); AT 2/2 (v)

Buy a dinosaur Children could be encouraged to put different prices on their dinosaurs and play the game during spare moments. Encourage them to colour using a colour code – 10p red, 5p blue and so on. The dinosaur could be displayed and questions asked such as: How much for all of the tail? Will the head be cheaper or more expensive than the tail?
National Curriculum: AT 1/2 (i, ii); AT 2/2 (iii, v)

Safe purses This game can be played with small groups of children as a reinforcement activity during spare moments. Children could draw round their hands and cut out the shapes. The hands could be displayed on a washing line to assist with learning to count in fives.
National Curriculum: AT 1/2 (i, ii); AT 2/2 (i, v)

Coin thief Children could work in small groups to discover how difficult it would be if 1ps and 5ps were missing. Encourage systematic recording. Is there a pattern to the results?
National Curriculum: AT 1/3 (iii, iv); AT 2/2 (iii, v)

Nine pence change Children could arrange the items in order from most expensive to least expensive using coins to make their values. They could also order the change obtained when buying various items.
National Curriculum: AT 1/3 (i); AT 2/2 (iii, v)

Dinosaur change Dinosaurs could be colour coded, for example all the 2ps coloured red, and the 3ps coloured blue. Children could total the different-coloured areas and record them systematically.
National Curriculum: AT 1/2 (i, ii); AT 2/2 (i, v)

Lose it Discuss the game in class and how it may be extended or adapted. Different ideas could be tried in class or used as another homework activity.
National Curriculum: AT 1/3 (i, iii); AT 2/2 (iii, v)

Buying five Labels could be photocopied and displayed with their value. This will encourage children to count in 2ps, 3ps, 4ps and so on. As a beginning to multiplication they could be asked how many 4p fizzy drinks could be bought for 12p.
National Curriculum: AT 1/2 (i, iii); AT 2/2 (iii, v)

Coin animal Animals could be displayed in values and questions asked: Is the largest animal the most expensive? Can you buy any two animals for 10p?
National Curriculum: AT 1/1 (i, ii); AT 2/1 (i)

TIME

My favourite day Children could sort themselves into favourite day groups and sit in a circle. You could play games, for example 'Stand up if your favourite day is before Wednesday/after Friday/a weekend day'. Children could stick their pictures on to a circle – each day being allotted a segment.
National Curriculum: AT 1/1 (ii, iii)

Day and night Make a large picture with the children's drawings to show day and night time activities.
National Curriculum: AT 1/2 (i, ii); AT 2/2 (viii)

Today, tomorrow, yesterday Make a circular day of the week display. Yesterday, today and tomorrow could be written on large arrows and children could take turns to move them to the relevant positions.
National Curriculum: AT 1/1 (i, ii); AT 5/1 (ii)

What shall I wear? Make a class book including everyone's picture. Discuss their reasons for choosing particular items of clothing.
National Curriculum: AT 1/1 (ii, ii); AT 5/1 (ii)

The apple tree Make a big circular season and month chart. Children could draw either apple or horse-chestnut trees. These pictures could surround the large chart. Ask questions such as: In which season do we pick apples?
National Curriculum: AT 1/1 (i, ii); AT 5/1 (i, ii)

Breakfast time Mark the time on the classroom clock with Blu-Tack before beginning an activity. Children will then be able to calculate how many minutes the activity took.
National Curriculum: AT 1/2 (i, ii); AT 2/2 (vii)

Measuring time Children may like to compare a digital 24-hour clock with an analogue clock. Perhaps they could learn the analogue time by reading the clock in the same way as a digital to begin with, e.g. 4.15 for quarter past four. Clocks the children have recorded could be grouped in a variety of ways. Order them by time and display them on a washing line with significant times written on, such as play time, news time.
National Curriculum: AT 1/2 (i, ii); AT 2/2 (vii)

Roman numbers Make number lines using a collection of different symbols and words, for example: Roman, Urdu and French.
National Curriculum: AT 1/2 (i, ii, iii)

Pace it out Can children estimate 30 seconds without looking at the clock? Perhaps they could learn a word and see how many times they can write it in 30 seconds.
National Curriculum: AT 1/2 (i, ii); AT 2/2 (viii)

My favourite TV programme Mark the time on the classroom clock with Blu-Tack so that children will be able to count the minutes spent on various activities throughout the day.
National Curriculum: AT 1/2 (i, ii); AT 2/2 (vii, viii)

Years go by You can make a large timeline in the classroom. Encourage the children to look at only the last two digits of the year number. This will help them to count on. Make sure they realise which year it is now! On your class timeline let the children write or draw all the events they have marked on their individual timelines. Talk about which year the children were born. Which year will they leave school? In what year will they be 20?
National Curriculum: AT 1/2 (i, ii); AT 2/2 (viii); AT 2/3 (i)

My family history Make a large timeline in the classroom to record significant events in the future and in the past.
National Curriculum: AT 1/1 (ii, iii)

Moon watch You could use a globe, a torch and a ball to demonstrate how the sun reflects on to the moon. The children could make a circular diagram to show the phases of the moon.
National Curriculum: AT 1/2 (i); AT 2/2 (viii)

Digital/analogue Children could sit in time order holding their clocks and play a game, for example: 'Stand up if your clock is something after seven o'clock'. Arrange the clocks in time order on a washing line. Children could draw pictures to show what happens at particular times.
National Curriculum: AT 1/2 (i, ii); AT 2/3 (xi)

In the wash Children could arrange their times in order. Questions could be asked, such as 'How many cycles took less than one hour?' If you had a template of a clock face the children could colour in the number of five minute intervals required to represent the cycle.
National Curriculum: AT 1/2 (i, ii); AT 2/2 (viii)

Eating times Children could discuss which meals took the longest and the shortest times. How many meals took less than ten minutes? Who ate for longer than an hour? You could 'mark' the class clock with a piece of Blu-Tack while children are involved in activities. It helps to concentrate the mind if they only have ten minutes to tidy up and they can see the minute hand travelling closer to the Blu-Tack.
National Curriculum: AT 1/2 (i, ii); AT 2/2 (vii, viii)

Hopalong Children could gather information for various races. You could set up an obstacle race so they could time themselves and record the data. Use circles divided into 12 segments to show five second intervals. Children can use these to record the information.
National Curriculum: AT 1/2 (i, ii); AT 2/2 (viii)

Travelling to work Children could gather information in groups. They could order walking times from longest to shortest. How many people cycle to work? Who makes the longest journey in their car?
National Curriculum: AT 1/2 (i, ii); AT 2/2 (viii)

24 hours in the day Make a large 24 hour clock. Shade in daylight and nighttime hours and write/draw significant happenings on the clock.
National Curriculum: AT 1/2 (i, ii); AT 2/3 (xi)

Just a minute Have a competition – children could work in pairs. How many times can you write a particular word in one minute? This is particularly useful for problem words: they, when, because, etc. Make a chart to show your results and write the words extra large as a reminder.
National Curriculum: AT 1/2 (i, ii); AT 2/2 (vii)

TEMPERATURE

Freezing cold Encourage the children to discuss why the times for melting varied. They could sit in time order holding their containers, then discuss the results.
National Curriculum: AT 1/1 (i, ii, iii); AT 2/2 (ii, vii)

Choosing clothes Children could sort their pictures to make a seasons/months collage.
National Curriculum: AT 1/1 (i, ii); AT 5/1 (i, ii)

Hot hands Children could take the temperature of the water in the different bowls. These could then be displayed with the thermometer showing the temperatures and the children's responses to the investigation.
National Curriculum: AT 1/2 (i, ii, iii)

Thermometer measures The school thermometer could be used to record temperatures in different parts of the classroom and playground. Children could estimate the readings first. This will promote conversations about wind chill factors, shady areas and so on.
National Curriculum: AT 1/2 (i, ii); AT 2/2 (vii)

Take three bottles

YOU WILL NEED: three bottles of various heights; a pencil and paper and some water.

● Order the bottles from tallest to shortest.

● Lie your bottles on their side and draw round them.

● Does the tallest bottle hold the most?

Dear Parent or Carer

It is important that your child can order objects and use descriptive vocabulary other than big and small. Use words like tall, taller, short, shorter, taller than, shorter than. If you have any other empty bottles your child may like to discover whether the tallest bottle holds the most.

National Curriculum reference: AT 1 and AT 2

_____and

child

_____

helper(s)

_____

did this activity together

_____and

child

_____

helper(s)

_____

did this activity together

Find three toys

YOU WILL NEED: 3 toys; a pencil and
paper.

● Find three toys and arrange them
into order of length.

● Draw round your toys on a piece
of paper.

impact MATHS HOMEWORK

Find five leaves

YOU WILL NEED: five leaves of different lengths; a pencil and paper and some crayons.

● Arrange your leaves in order of length.

● Now draw round the leaves and colour them in.

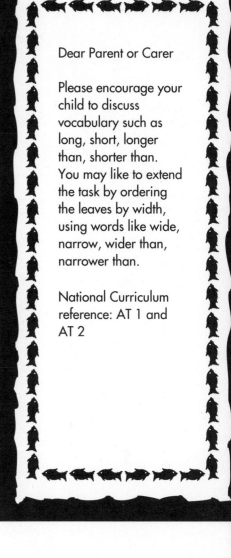

Dear Parent or Carer

Please encourage your child to discuss vocabulary such as long, short, longer than, shorter than. You may like to extend the task by ordering the leaves by width, using words like wide, narrow, wider than, narrower than.

National Curriculum reference: AT 1 and AT 2

_____and

child

_____

helper(s)

_____

did this activity together

_____and

child

_____

helper(s)

_____

did this activity together

Shoes

YOU WILL NEED: 3 shoes; a pencil; crayons and paper.

● Find 3 shoes at home that have different widths.

● Draw round the shoes and colour the outlines in carefully.

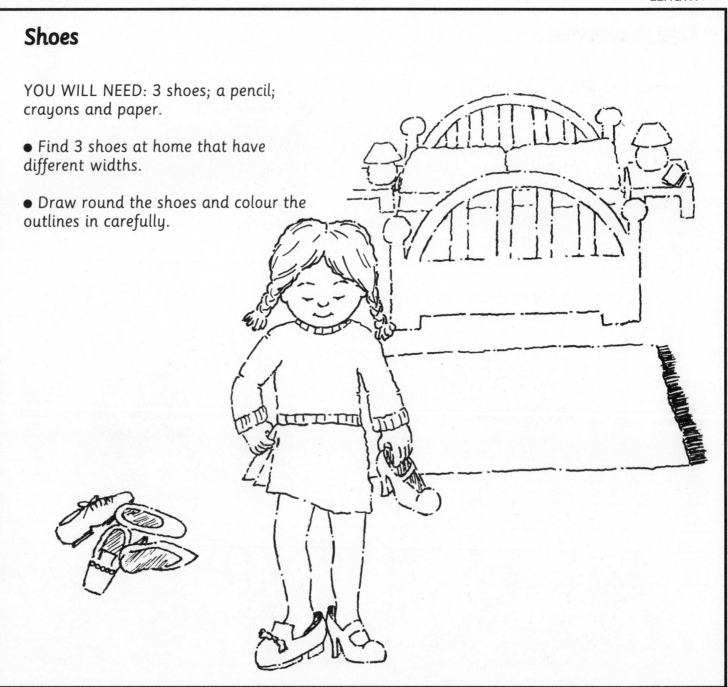

impact MATHS HOMEWORK

Teddy's headband

YOU WILL NEED: scissors; string; paper and a pencil.

● Can you make a headband to fit round teddy's head? Make sure it fits exactly – teddy doesn't want a headache!

● Decorate the headband and write your name on it.

● Will your teddy's headband fit around anything else at home? Try measuring some bottles, bowls and mugs. What about other toy's heads, arms or legs?

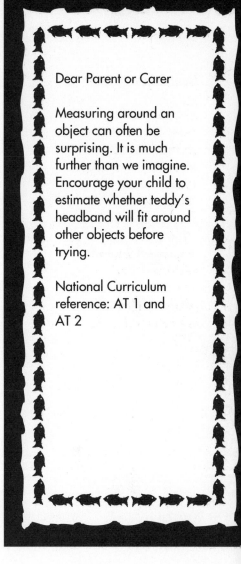

Dear Parent or Carer

Measuring around an object can often be surprising. It is much further than we imagine. Encourage your child to estimate whether teddy's headband will fit around other objects before trying.

National Curriculum reference: AT 1 and AT 2

_____and

child

_____

helper(s)

_____

did this activity together

Dear Parent or Carer

Help your child to make their chain if this is a problem. Discuss why some chains are longer than others. Which daisies make the longest chain? Where can you find the longest daisies?

National Curriculum reference: AT 1 and AT 2

_____and

child

_____

helper(s)

_____

did this activity together

Daisy chains

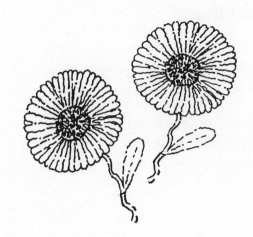

YOU WILL NEED: several people to do this activity with you on a lawn or in the park; a pencil and paper.

● Each person must make a daisy chain using five daisies.

● Order your daisy chains by length.

● Draw round your favourite daisy chain on a piece of paper or the back of this sheet.

impact MATHS HOMEWORK

Long or wide?

YOU WILL NEED: some long strips of paper; Sellotape; scissors and a pencil.

● Ask someone at home to help you cut a strip of paper that is exactly the length of your body.

● Now stretch out your arms as wide as possible and make another strip to measure your width.

● Write width/length and your name on to your strip. Keep your strips side by side.

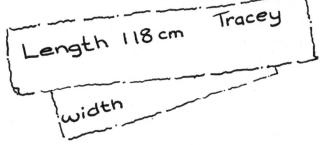

Length 118 cm   Tracey

width

● Try this with other members of your family. Do you notice anything?

Dear Parent or Carer

You could suggest marking the length and width of your child using books. They can then cut their own strips of paper using the distance along the line as a guide. You could estimate and measure the strips using handspans.

National Curriculum reference: AT 1 and AT 2

_____and

child

_____

helper(s)

_____

did this activity together

Me and my helper

Dear Parent or Carer

We are comparing many lengths at the moment and starting to realise that we need to use a unit of measurement. This activity will help your child to understand this concept.

National Curriculum reference: AT 1 and AT 2

YOU WILL NEED: string; scissors and a pencil.

How many times taller than you is your partner?

● Lie down on the floor. Ask your partner to cut a piece of string exactly your length.

● Now ask them to lie down on the floor and see how many times you can fit your piece of string along them!

● In the box below draw your partner and write the number of times the string fitted beside your drawing.

_____and

child

_____

helper(s)

_____

did this activity together

impact MATHS HOMEWORK

Am I square?

Are you as tall as you are wide (with your arms stretched out of course!)?

● Lie down on the floor.

● Ask your partner to make a line of objects beside you which is as long as you are – they could use books, magazines, spoons, pencils or anything else that comes to hand, but the line must be the same length as you!

● Stand up carefully. Now lie down with your arms stretched wide along the line. (You will have to put your head over the line!) Is the line longer or shorter than your arms?

● Draw a picture of your line of objects and ask your partner to say whether you were taller than you are wide, or wider than you are tall, or are you square?

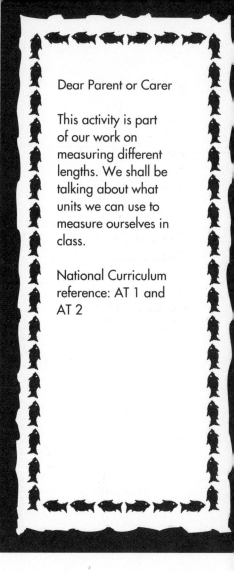

Dear Parent or Carer

This activity is part of our work on measuring different lengths. We shall be talking about what units we can use to measure ourselves in class.

National Curriculum reference: AT 1 and AT 2

_____and

child

_____

helper(s)

_____

did this activity together

Dear Parent or Carer

Discuss which leaves would be suitable for measuring. If your child wants to use different sizes, that is fine. We will be discussing why we need a standard size for measuring back in the classroom.

National Curriculum reference: AT 1 and AT 2

_____and

child

_____

helper(s)

_____

did this activity together

How tall is teddy?

YOU WILL NEED: some leaves; paper and a pencil and your teddy.

● Draw round your teddy on a piece of paper and estimate his height in leaves. Write down your guess in the space below. Now measure your teddy in leaves and draw round the leaves used. Count them and write in the correct number.

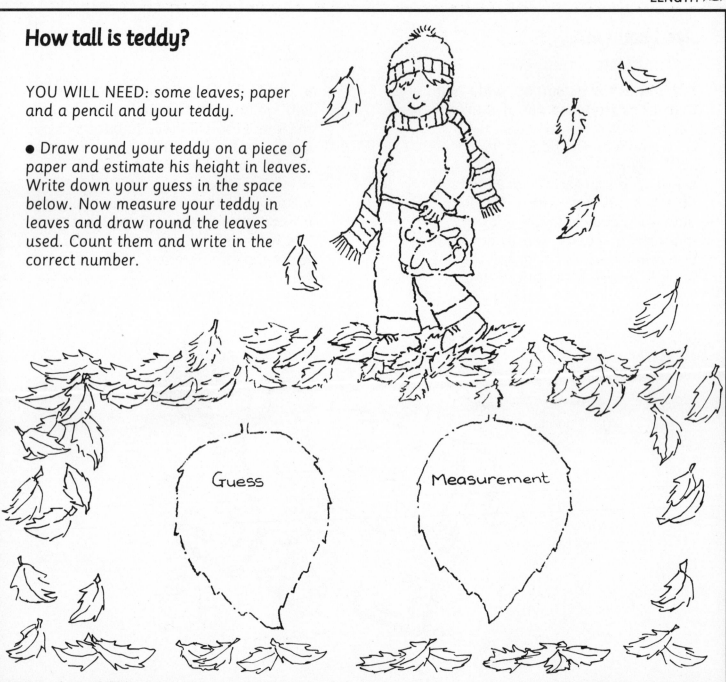

Guess

Measurement

impact MATHS HOMEWORK

How fat is teddy?

YOU WILL NEED: scissors; something that will bend – string or a paper strip; a pencil and a teaspoon.

> **How will you measure round teddy's tummy?**

● First of all, cut a piece of string or paper as an estimate. Fit it round teddy – don't make him sick!

● Is your strip of paper longer or shorter than teddy?

● Now cut a piece of paper that is exactly the right length to fit round teddy, then write your name on it.

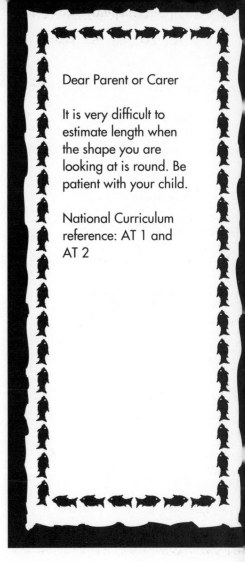

Dear Parent or Carer

It is very difficult to estimate length when the shape you are looking at is round. Be patient with your child.

National Curriculum reference: AT 1 and AT 2

_____and
child

_____
helper(s)

_____

did this activity together

Find a plate

_____and

child

_____

helper(s)

_____

did this activity together

YOU WILL NEED: a plate; a pencil and some paper.

● Choose a plate and draw round it on a piece of paper or the back of this sheet. (Remember to decorate your drawing.)

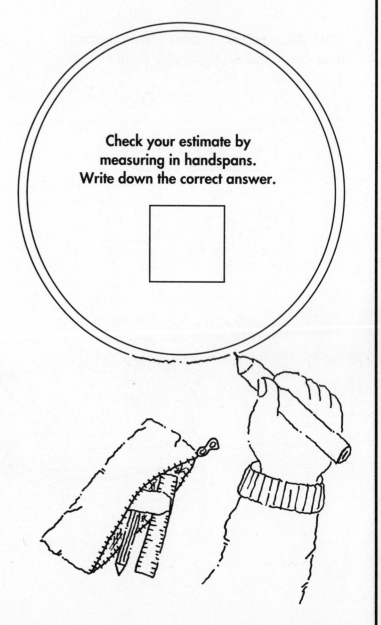

Check your estimate by measuring in handspans. Write down the correct answer.

How far is it round the edge of your plate? How many handspans do you think it will take?

impact MATHS HOMEWORK

Book perimeters

YOU WILL NEED: card, such as a cereal box; scissors and a pencil.

The perimeter is the distance round an object.

● Cut a piece of card the length of your handspan.

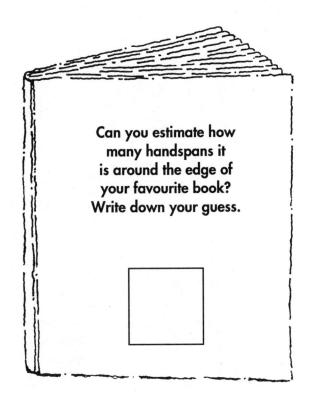

Can you estimate how many handspans it is around the edge of your favourite book? Write down your guess.

● As you measure and count do you want to change your estimate?

● Write down your new guess – if you have one!

● What was the correct answer?

Did you estimate too many or too few handspans?

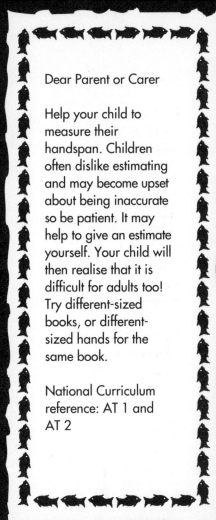

Dear Parent or Carer

Help your child to measure their handspan. Children often dislike estimating and may become upset about being inaccurate so be patient. It may help to give an estimate yourself. Your child will then realise that it is difficult for adults too! Try different-sized books, or different-sized hands for the same book.

National Curriculum reference: AT 1 and AT 2

_____and

child

_____

helper(s)

_____

did this activity together

Dear Parent or Carer

You may need to help your child with measuring to ensure that they do not overlap the handspan card. Be careful to count each handspan as you measure.

National Curriculum reference: AT 1 and AT 2

_____and

child

_____

helper(s)

_____

did this activity together

IMPACT perimeters

YOU WILL NEED: card such as a cereal box; scissors and a pencil.

● Cut a piece of card the length of your handspan.

● How many do you think will fit round the edge or perimeter of this activity sheet? Write down your estimate. Which sides will use the most/least handspans?

● Now measure it and write down the correct answer.

estimate

perimeter

impact MATHS HOMEWORK

The fattest bottle

- Copy or cut out the decimetre strip at the bottom of the page and stick it on to card.

- Gather together a selection of bottles (ask first!) and try to order the bottles from the fattest to the thinnest.

- Before you begin measuring, estimate how far it is round each bottle.

- Now measure round your bottles. What are you using for measuring?

_____

- Stretch out whatever you use each time and measure it with your decimetre strip. Write down the measurements of your bottles below.

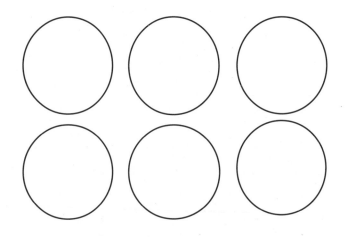

Dear Parent or Carer

A decimetre is 10cm long. Please ask your child what could be used for measuring round their bottles. It will need to bend! To extend the activity you could re-order the bottles by height. Are the orders the same? Does the fattest bottle hold the most?

National Curriculum reference: AT 1 and AT 2

_____and

child

_____

helper(s)

_____

did this activity together

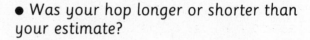

Hopping

You will have to concentrate, as you are going to make a very long hop!

● Put a marker down where you are going to start and where you think you are going to land. Measure how far this is. Write it down.

Off you go – HOP.

● Was your hop longer or shorter than your estimate?

● Measure your hop – use your foot or a ruler as a measure. Write it down.

● Now ask other members of your family to try. Record their estimates and measured hops on the chart below.

name	estimate	distance

_____and

child

_____

helper(s)

_____

did this activity together

Decimetre measure

A decimetre is 10 centimetres long. There are 10 decimetres in a metre.

● Estimate the height of each member of your family in decimetres. Write down your guesses in the chart below.

Family member	Guess

● Now copy or cut out the decimetre strip at the bottom of the page and use it to check your estimates.

● Use strips of squared paper to draw your family. (1 centimetre square represents a decimetre.)

```
0          5          10
```

Dear Parent or Carer

Give your child time to estimate. It is often easier to estimate the shortest person (or pet) first.

National Curriculum reference: AT 1 and AT 2

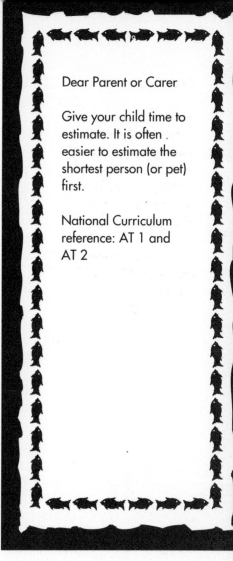

_____and

child

_____

helper(s)

_____

did this activity together

Dear Parent or Carer

Try to encourage your child to estimate before measuring; this will help with concentrating on the task. Talk about which shapes are easiest to measure.

National Curriculum reference: AT 1 and AT 2

_____and

child

_____

helper(s)

_____

did this activity together

Exactly twenty centimetres

YOU WILL NEED: card such as a cereal box; scissors; paper and a pencil.

● Copy or cut out the 20cm strip at the bottom of the page and stick it on to card.

● Now find three things at home that are exactly 20cms long (or round). Draw them on a piece of paper and bring them into school with your 20cm strip.

● How many 20cm strips do you need to make a metre?

1 metre = 20 x ☐

0   5   10   15   20

Quarter my height

YOU WILL NEED: paper or string;
scissors and a pencil.

● Ask someone at home to help you cut
a strip of paper or a piece of string the
same length as your height.

● Bring a quarter of the strip to school
with your name on it. How did you find
a quarter of your strip?

Dear Parent or Carer

Give your child time to
consider quartering the
strip of paper. You
may like to write down
how your child solved
the problem.

National Curriculum
reference: AT 1 and
AT 2

_____and

child

_____

helper(s)

_____

did this activity together

_____and

child

_____

helper(s)

_____

did this activity together

Race to one metre

YOU WILL NEED: 2 dice; a metre measure; 20 decimetre strips and 20 centimetre strips.

● Make 20 decimetre and 20 centimetre strips like the ones at the bottom of the page then place them in a central pile.

● Take turns to throw the 2 dice.

● Each player adds their 2 scores together and takes that number of centimetre strips from the pile.

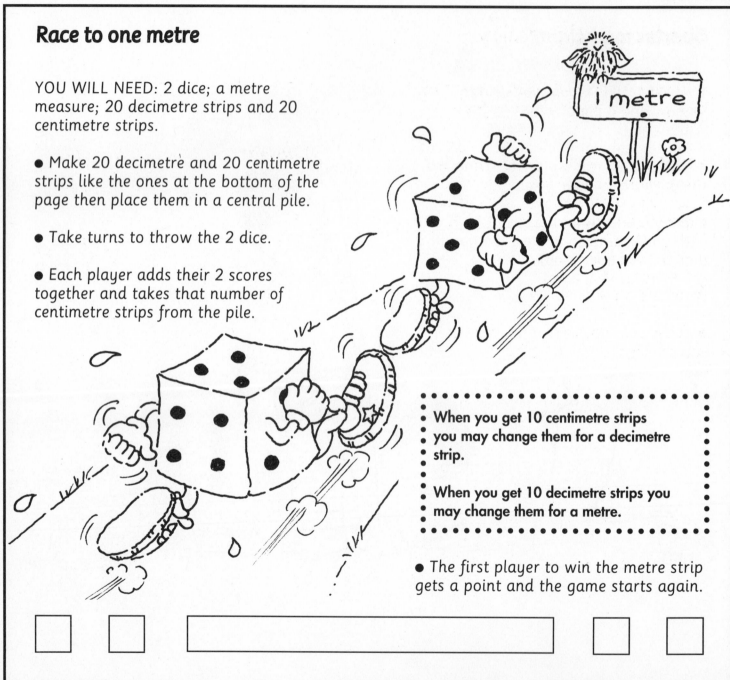

When you get 10 centimetre strips you may change them for a decimetre strip.

When you get 10 decimetre strips you may change them for a metre.

● The first player to win the metre strip gets a point and the game starts again.

impact MATHS HOMEWORK

Hands along the window

● Choose a window in your house. How many of your hands fit along the window?

● So that you don't make finger prints, ask someone to help you draw round your outstretched hand on a piece of paper. Cut it out.

● Now count how many of these hands will fit around your window. Write down the answer.

● In the space below draw what you can see from your window.

hands

Dear Parent or Carer

This activity helps children to learn that measuring involves repeating a unit.
In this case the unit of measurement is their hand! Help them to measure the window without leaving gaps between their hands.

National Curriculum reference: AT 1 and AT 2

_____and

child

_____

helper(s)

_____

did this activity together

_____and

child

_____

helper(s)

_____

did this activity together

Shared metre daisy chain

You will need some friends to help, either in the park or on a lawn.

We began making our chain at:

There were ____ **people.**

_____ **made the longest**

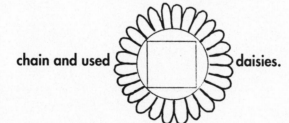

chain and used ____ **daisies.**

Did the longest chain use the most daisies?

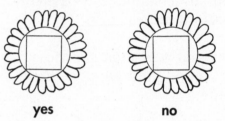

yes   no

We finished our metre daisy chain at:

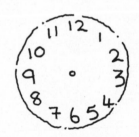

We took ____ **minutes.**

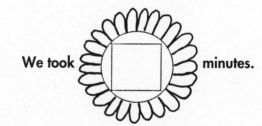

impact MATHS HOMEWORK

A new leaf

YOU WILL NEED: a leaf; a decimetre strip like the one at the bottom of the page; Lego bricks and a pencil and paper.

● Choose a leaf to measure, using the decimetre strip, bricks or Lego. Write down your answers.

I began measuring at:

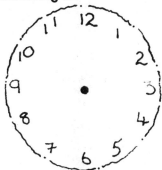

I finished measuring at:

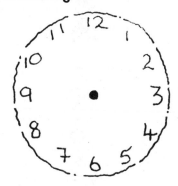

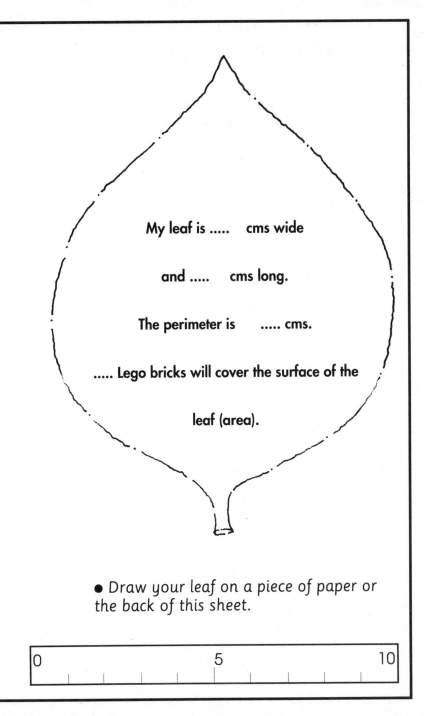

My leaf is ..... cms wide

and ..... cms long.

The perimeter is ..... cms.

..... Lego bricks will cover the surface of the

leaf (area).

● Draw your leaf on a piece of paper or the back of this sheet.

```
0              5              10
```

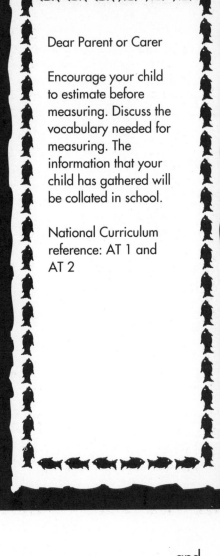

Dear Parent or Carer

Encourage your child to estimate before measuring. Discuss the vocabulary needed for measuring. The information that your child has gathered will be collated in school.

National Curriculum reference: AT 1 and AT 2

_____and

child

_____

helper(s)

_____

did this activity together

_____and

child

_____

helper(s)

_____

did this activity together

Measuring

Around the table

YOU WILL NEED: card, such as a cereal box; scissors and a pencil.

The perimeter is the distance round the edge of an object.

● Copy or cut out the 20cm strip at the bottom of the page and stick it on to card.

● How many strips will fit around the edge of your table?

● Estimate before you measure and ask your family for their guesses. Write them down in the box opposite.

● How many of your strips will make a metre?

**strips make
a metre**

● Do you think the perimeter will be:

☐ **more than a metre**

☐ **less than a metre?**

family member	guess
actual perimeter	

● Now measure your table. Whose estimate was the closest? Write down your table perimeter.

| 0 | 5 | 10 | 15 | 20 |

Book measures

YOU WILL NEED: some string; a book and a pencil.

How long will a piece of string need to be to fit around your book?

● Very carefully lay a piece of string all the way around your book and cut it off at the right length.

● Now measure your piece of string. How long is it?

My piece of string is _____ **cms**

● Draw a picture of your favourite books below.

Dear Parent or Carer

This activity helps us to practise measuring using centimetres. It is important that children develop the skills of estimating in centimetres and checking their measurements. Help them to guess first.

National Curriculum reference: AT 1 and AT 2

_____and

child

_____

helper(s)

_____

did this activity together

_____and

child

_____

helper(s)

_____

did this activity together

Measure a box

YOU WILL NEED: a smallish box to measure; a ruler or tape; marbles, Lego or small bricks.

● Look at the time. Draw the time you begin on this clock.

I began measuring at:

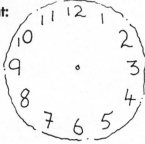

● Now look at your box and begin measuring. Write down your answers.

My box is   **centimetres long.**

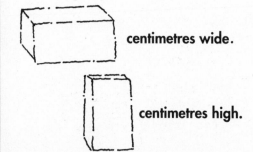

centimetres wide.

centimetres high.

● Fill your box with marbles or bricks.

My box will hold

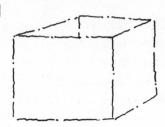

This is its capacity.

I finished measuring at:

It took   **minutes to measure my box.**

impact MATHS HOMEWORK

Measure your shoe

YOU WILL NEED: a suitably sized shoe; a tape measure or ruler and some small bricks, Lego or marbles.

● Look at the time. Draw the time you begin on the clock below.

I began measuring at:

● Now look at your shoe and begin measuring. Write down your answers.

My shoe is

☐ centimetres wide

☐ centimetres long

☐ centimetres high.

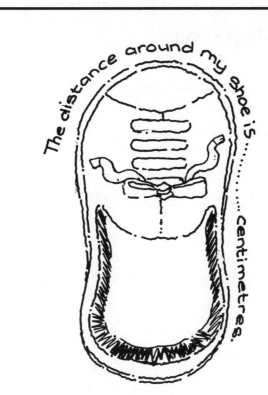

The distance around my shoe is .... centimetres.

I finished measuring at:

It took ☐ minutes.

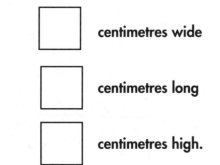

Dear Parent or Carer

Encourage your child to estimate before measuring. Ask questions, such as: How much longer/shorter do you think this measurement will be compared to the last one? Discuss which shoe would be the most suitable for measuring.

National Curriculum reference: AT 1 and AT 2

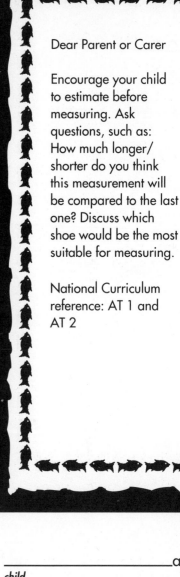

_____and

child

_____

helper(s)

_____

did this activity together

_____and

child

_____

helper(s)

_____

did this activity together

Turning a wheel

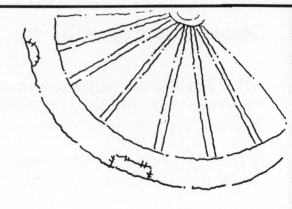

● Choose a wheel – it could be on a pram, bicycle, go-cart... You are going to measure how far your wheel will travel in one revolution.

> THINGS TO THINK ABOUT:
> Where will you start measuring?
> How will you know when your wheel has turned once?
> How will you measure the distance?

● Make a newspaper wheel of the same size and cut a strip of paper to show how far the wheel travelled in one revolution.

impact MATHS HOMEWORK

Diameter and circumference

● Make several circle shapes. (Draw round plates, bowls, tins, jars, etc.)

● Diameter is the distance across the centre of a circle.

● Circumference is the distance around the edge of a circle.

● Now make a strip of paper to show the length of the circumference of each circle and cut a strip to show the length of the diameter. Stick your diameter strips on to your circumference strip.

● Do you notice anything?

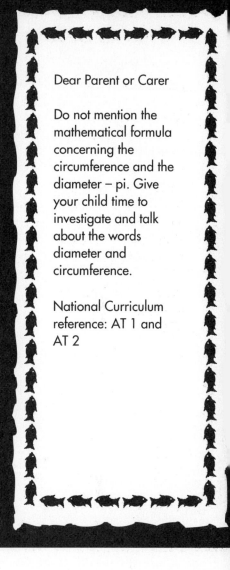

Dear Parent or Carer

Do not mention the mathematical formula concerning the circumference and the diameter – pi. Give your child time to investigate and talk about the words diameter and circumference.

National Curriculum reference: AT 1 and AT 2

_____and

child

_____

helper(s)

_____

did this activity together

_____and

child

_____

helper(s)

_____

did this activity together

Framing a picture

YOU WILL NEED: card, such as a cereal box; scissors and a pencil.

● Copy or cut out the decimetre strip at the bottom of the page and stick it on to card.

● Now choose your favourite picture in the house. If the frame costs 20p per decimetre how much will it cost to frame your favourite picture? Take a guess and write it down.

● Now measure the frame using the card strip and write down the correct amount.

impact MATHS HOMEWORK

Lace borders

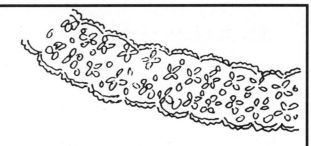

YOU WILL NEED: card such as a cereal box; scissors and a pencil.

It is Granny's birthday. You are going to decorate a plain hanky as a special present but before going to the shop you will need to know certain things.

● Copy or cut out the decimetre strip at the bottom of the page and stick it on to card.

● Find a hanky or a piece of paper of similar size to use.

● Measure the distance around the edge of the hanky.

● Lace for edging your hanky costs 25p per decimetre. How much money will it cost to decorate it?

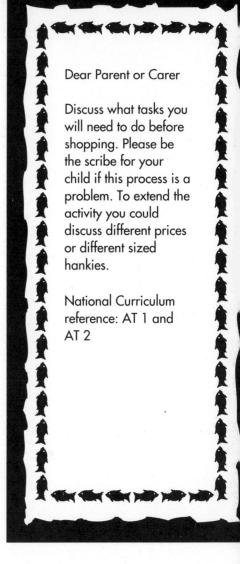

Dear Parent or Carer

Discuss what tasks you will need to do before shopping. Please be the scribe for your child if this process is a problem. To extend the activity you could discuss different prices or different sized hankies.

National Curriculum reference: AT 1 and AT 2

_____and

child

_____

helper(s)

_____

did this activity together

_____and

child

_____

helper(s)

_____

did this activity together

Which colours are easiest to see?

Blue

Blue

Yellow

Yellow

● Colour in the numbers as indicated.

● Now ask someone to hold the cards up, in turn, 20 paces away. Which numbers can you see most clearly?

● Try the same activity 40 paces away. Is the result the same?

● Write down your observations on a piece of paper.

impact MATHS HOMEWORK

Does it fit?

YOU WILL NEED: two pieces of paper; a pencil and felt-tipped pens or crayons.

● Find one of your shoes. Place it on a piece of paper and draw carefully round it.

● Colour in the shape and label it 'My shoe'.

● Now put your bare foot on a piece of paper and ask someone to draw around that!

● Colour in the shape. Label it 'My foot'.

● Cut both shapes out carefully.

● Does your foot shape fit on your shoe shape? Which is bigger?

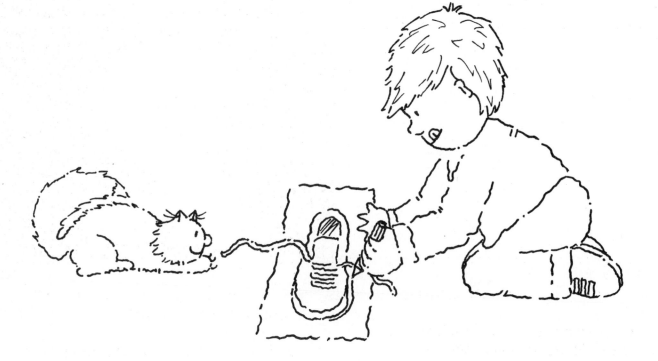

Dear Parent or Carer

This activity will help your child to develop an idea of area – the amount of ground covered. We shall be talking about larger and smaller in relation to area in class.

National Curriculum reference: AT 1 and AT 2

_____and

child

_____

helper(s)

_____

did this activity together

Square foot

YOU WILL NEED: squared paper and a pencil.

● Ask someone to help you draw round your foot on the squared paper.

● Count how many squares are inside the outline of your foot.

● Write down your answer.

My foot is ⬜ **squares**

_____ and

child

_____

helper(s)

did this activity together

Tin areas

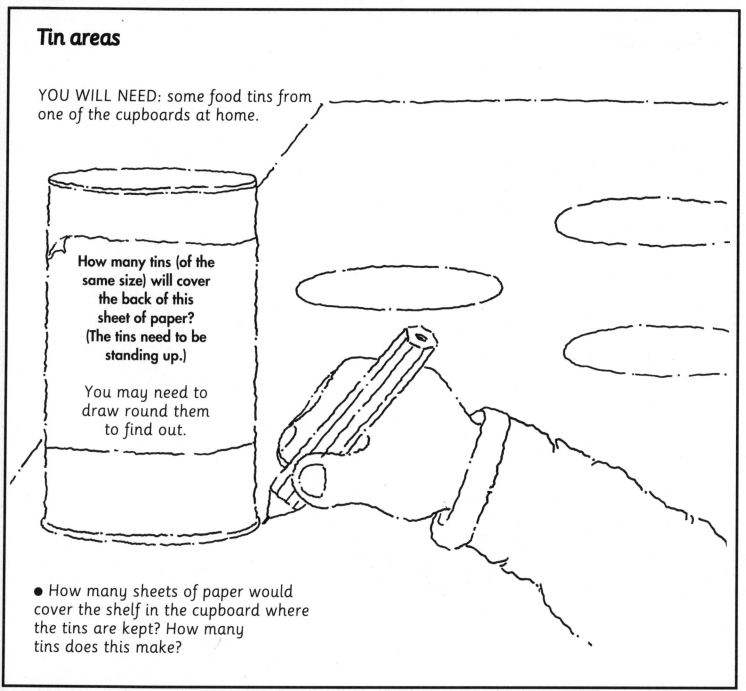

YOU WILL NEED: some food tins from one of the cupboards at home.

How many tins (of the same size) will cover the back of this sheet of paper? (The tins need to be standing up.)

You may need to draw round them to find out.

● How many sheets of paper would cover the shelf in the cupboard where the tins are kept? How many tins does this make?

Dear Parent or Carer

This activity leads towards work calculating areas through multiplication (the number of rows times the number of columns). Encourage your child to line the tins up along one edge, and then along the other edge of the paper, then try to work out the area without drawing in every single tin.

National Curriculum reference: AT 1 and AT 2

_____and

child

_____

helper(s)

_____

did this activity together

_____and

child

_____

helper(s)

_____

did this activity together

Toy areas

YOU WILL NEED: squared paper; a pencil and crayons.

Find a toy you like which is not too large.

- Put it on the squared paper and draw carefully around it.

- Colour in the shape then count the squares you have coloured.

- How many squares makes its area?

My teddy is

squares

impact MATHS HOMEWORK

Square metres

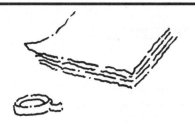

YOU WILL NEED: a piece of string measuring one metre; some sheets of paper or newspaper; some Sellotape and lots of patience!

● You need to make a square metre using newspaper or paper. Use your piece of string to measure it, and your Sellotape to stick the pieces of paper together.

● When you have made your square metre, can you find some things which will fit on it? (You could use cushions, or shoes or plates, or hankies – clean ones! – or anything else you think of!)

● Count how many of each object will fit on your square metre and write down the answers.

● You could choose one object and draw round as many of them as you can on your square metre.

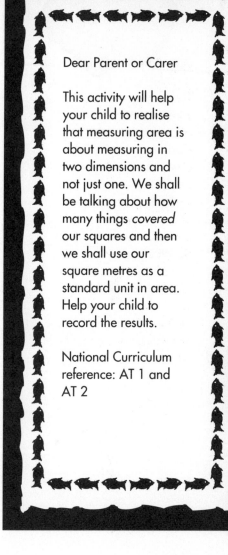

Dear Parent or Carer

This activity will help your child to realise that measuring area is about measuring in two dimensions and not just one. We shall be talking about how many things *covered* our squares and then we shall use our square metres as a standard unit in area. Help your child to record the results.

National Curriculum reference: AT 1 and AT 2

_____and

child

_____

helper(s)

_____

did this activity together

_____and

child

_____

helper(s)

_____

did this activity together

Dinosaur tiles

● Cut out the tiles from the accompanying sheet. (They will be easier to use if you stick them onto the back of an old Christmas or birthday card.)

● Draw a dinosaur on each one.

● Now use them to measure the area of one thing in your home. It could be a newspaper or magazine, a small table, a chair seat, the TV screen … Count how many tiles it takes to cover it.

● Write down the object you chose to measure and number of tiles you used.

● Can you find the areas of other objects? Write down your results in the chart.

object	number of tiles

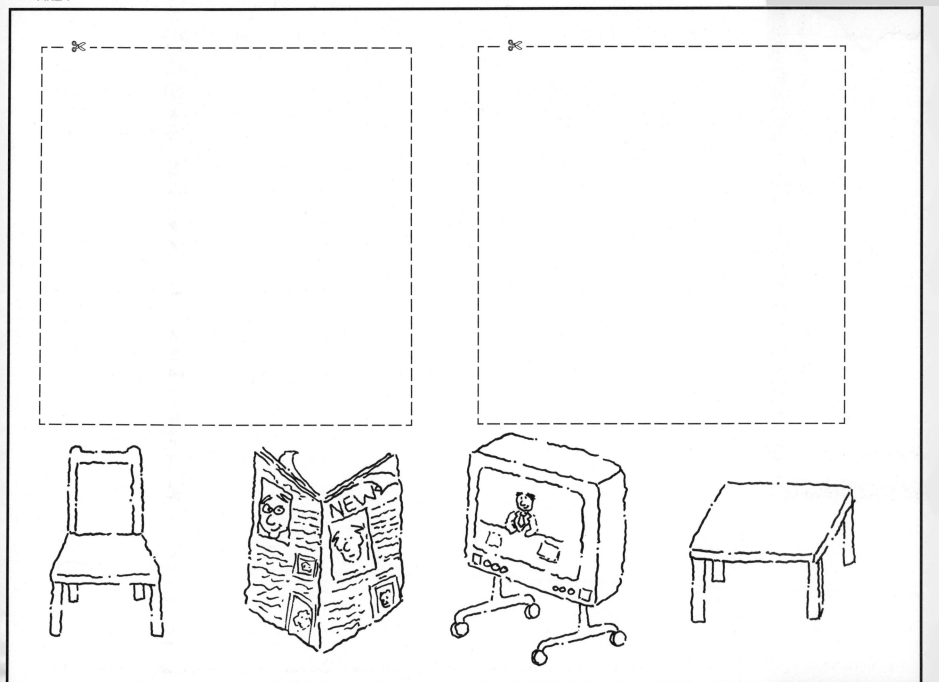

_____and

child

_____

helper(s)

_____

did this activity together

Book at bedtime

Find a book – preferably one that you read at bedtime!

You are going to use a book to measure the area of your bed!

● Count how many times your book fits along the length of your bed. This is the number of rows.

● Count how many times the book fits along the width. This is the number of columns.

● How many of your book do you think it will take to cover your bed? How can you work this out?

● Write down your answers.

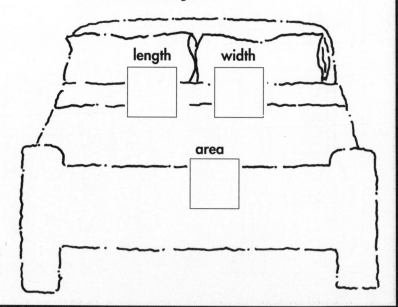

length

width

area

impact MATHS HOMEWORK

Area count up

YOU WILL NEED: a pack of cards and your favourite book.

● Lay out some cards on top of your book. Make sure that it is covered but do not let the cards overlap!

● How many cards did it take to cover your book?

● Draw your book with the right number of cards on it in the box below.

● Now add up the values of all the cards. How many points is your book worth?

My book is worth

Dear Parent or Carer

This activity will help your child to realise that area is the measurement of the amount of space *covered*, that is to say it is measurement in two dimensions.
We shall be comparing the areas of our books back in class, and discussing what else we can use to measure area.

National Curriculum reference: AT 1 and AT 2

_____and

child

_____

helper(s)

_____

did this activity together

_____and

child

_____

helper(s)

_____

did this activity together

Best rooms

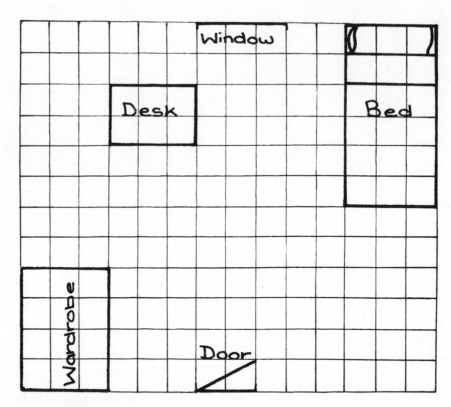

YOU WILL NEED: squared paper; a nice sharp pencil and someone to help you!

● You are going to draw a plan of one of the rooms where you live. Choose the room you like the best!

● First of all count how long your room is in paces – you may have to guess a bit if you cannot pace it all!

● Now count how wide it is in paces.

● Draw the shape of the room in outline on the squared paper. Make it one square for every one pace long, and one square for every one pace wide. As in the example above, Don't forget any extra spaces!

● Now draw in the furniture and indicate on your plan where the windows and doors are.

● You can colour it all in if you like.

impact MATHS HOMEWORK

New areas

YOU WILL NEED: scissors; paper; a pencil and crayons.

The oblong below has an area of 12 squares.

● Cut it out, and cut out each of the squares.

● Now re-arrange the squares to make a new shape. Each of the squares must touch at least one other square – but none of them must overlap. You must use all 12 squares.

● Draw round your new shape and colour it in.

● What is the area of your new shape?

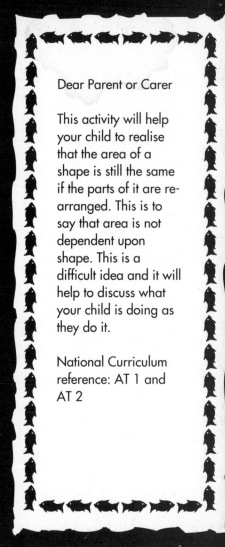

Dear Parent or Carer

This activity will help your child to realise that the area of a shape is still the same if the parts of it are re-arranged. This is to say that area is not dependent upon shape. This is a difficult idea and it will help to discuss what your child is doing as they do it.

National Curriculum reference: AT 1 and AT 2

_____and

child

_____

helper(s)

_____

did this activity together

_____and

child

_____

helper(s)

_____

did this activity together

Head areas

YOU WILL NEED: a largish piece of card like the back of a cereal packet.

● Lie down and rest your head on the piece of card.

● Ask someone to draw around your head on the card.

● Now cut out the shape of your head.

● Cut out the small square drawn below. How many times will this square fit on your head shape? You will need to draw round the square to count. (It will help to stick your small square on to its own piece of card to make it easier to draw round.)

● Write down your answer on your head shape.

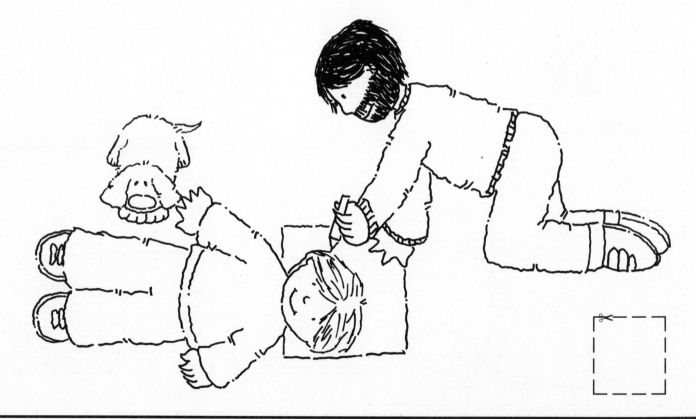

impact MATHS HOMEWORK

Coin areas

Which coin covers the largest area?

● Find an example of each of the coins we use.

● Look at the coins. Lay them out in order of area – from the one you think is the largest, to the one you think is the smallest area.

● Write down your order in the chart.

coin	guess	area

● Draw round each coin on the tiny squares below then count how many squares each one covers. If the coin covers more than half a square then count it. Don't count it otherwise.

● Write down the area of each coin in the chart. Colour the coin outlines in.

● Now study the order. Were you right?

_____and

child

_____

helper(s)

_____

did this activity together

_____and

child

_____

helper(s)

_____

did this activity together

Flat fruits

YOU WILL NEED: squared paper; a piece of fruit; a pencil and some crayons.

- Find a piece of fruit.

- Draw round it on the squared paper.

- Colour it in.

- Count how many squares your drawing covers and write down the number on the squared paper next to your drawing.

impact MATHS HOMEWORK

Fitting together

YOU WILL NEED: card; scissors and a pencil.

● Look at the shapes on this page.

● Cut them out and, if possible, stick them on to card. (Cut round them again, so you have a shape to draw round.)

● Which shapes will fit together repeatedly without leaving any gaps? Which ones leave gaps?

● Draw a pattern with one of the shapes which DOES fit together.

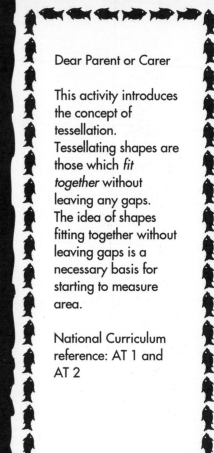

Dear Parent or Carer

This activity introduces the concept of tessellation. Tessellating shapes are those which *fit together* without leaving any gaps. The idea of shapes fitting together without leaving gaps is a necessary basis for starting to measure area.

National Curriculum reference: AT 1 and AT 2

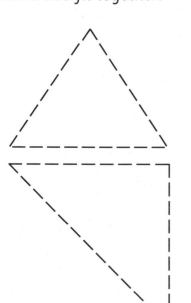
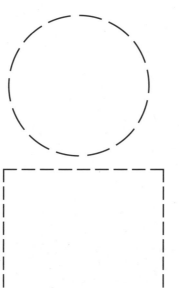

_____and

child

_____

helper(s)

_____

did this activity together

_____and

child

_____

helper(s)

_____

did this activity together

T-shirt cover up

● Spread out a T-shirt on the floor. (A vest will do if you can't find one!)

● Find as many flat things as you can to cover your T-shirt.

You could use – cards, envelopes, old letters, cassette tape boxes, empty matchboxes or anything else that comes to hand!

● When you have covered it with things – without any of them overlapping – draw a picture of your T-shirt on a piece of paper or the back of this sheet and carefully draw ALL the things on it.

● Don't forget to put away all the things afterwards.

impact MATHS HOMEWORK

Drink up

- What is your favourite drink?

- Look at the containers. Colour in the one you drink it from.

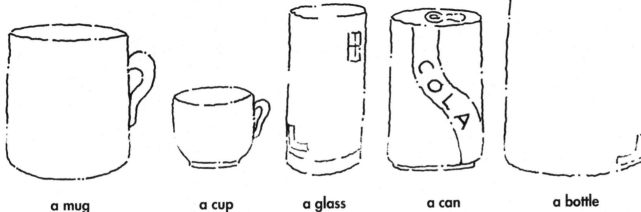

| **a mug** | **a cup** | **a glass** | **a can** | **a bottle** |

- When you start to drink is the mug/cup/glass/can/bottle:

  ☐ full?

  ☐ half full?

  ☐ less than half full?

- Do you drink it all?

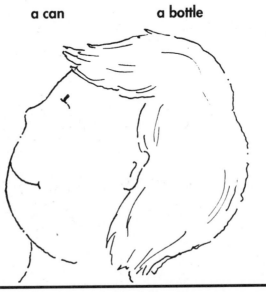

Dear Parent or Carer

This activity will help your child to understand that we can compare the capacity of different containers. The question of how full it is, or whether it is half empty, is important here. Talk about these ideas with your child.

National Curriculum reference: AT 1 and AT 2

_____and

child

_____

helper(s)

_____

did this activity together

impact MATHS HOMEWORK

Making containers

YOU WILL NEED: a piece of card; scissors; glue; paper clips and a pencil.

● Use the piece of card to make a container of any shape you like.

You may cut, stick, fold, clip, etc, as much as you like!

● Put you name on your container.

_____and

child

_____

helper(s)

_____

did this activity together

impact MATHS HOMEWORK

Balloon capacity

YOU WILL NEED: a balloon; a tablespoon; a bowl and somewhere – like the bath – where it does not matter if you get wet!

● First of all ask someone to blow up your balloon. (Do NOT tie the end!)

● Write down its capacity in tablespoonfuls.

My balloon held [ ] Spoonfuls

● Let the balloon go down. Now fill it with water. Fill it as full as you can!

● Tip the water (this is tricky!) into a bowl.

● Use a tablespoon to measure how much water your balloon held.

Dear Parent or Carer

This activity is an unusual way of getting children to measure the capacity of an object. They must measure the amount of water the balloon held using a tablespoon. This is great fun but very messy!

National Curriculum reference: AT 1 and AT 2

_____and

child

_____

helper(s)

_____

did this activity together

Dear Parent or Carer

This activity can be messy! It is worthwhile because it develops a very useful skill – that of estimating the capacity of a container. We are also going to be measuring the capacities of different containers in class.

National Curriculum reference: AT 1 and AT 2

_____and

child

_____

helper(s)

_____

did this activity together

Up to the brim

YOU WILL NEED: a saucepan and a cup; a pencil and water.

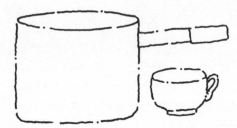

● Guess how many cups of water will fit in the saucepan.

● Ask other people in your home to guess too. Write down their guesses in the chart below.

person	guess

● To measure, fill the cup with water and tip it into the saucepan. Do this as many times as you have to in order to fill the saucepan. Count carefully how many cups you tip in.

● Write down the answer.

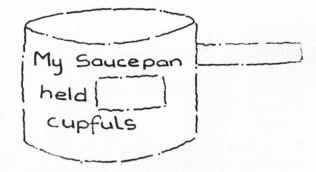

My Saucepan held [   ] cupfuls

● Whose guess was closest?

impact MATHS HOMEWORK

L-driver

When we buy orange juice or apple juice – or even milk, we may see an 'L' on the packet.

This L stands for litre.

How much is a litre?

● Cruise around your home – the kitchen will be the best place – and find a container that holds exactly one litre.

● Do not empty out its contents! Ask someone if you can have it – they may have to store the contents in something else!

● You could try cutting an old plastic bottle down to size if you can't find one that holds exactly one litre. (You will need to measure to make sure it holds one litre. How will you do this?)

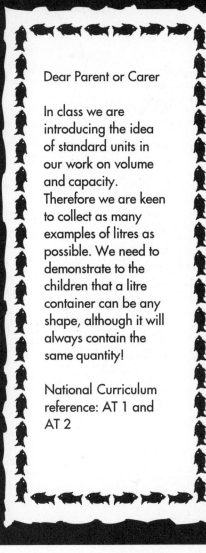

Dear Parent or Carer

In class we are introducing the idea of standard units in our work on volume and capacity. Therefore we are keen to collect as many examples of litres as possible. We need to demonstrate to the children that a litre container can be any shape, although it will always contain the same quantity!

National Curriculum reference: AT 1 and AT 2

_____and

child

_____

helper(s)

_____

did this activity together

_____and

child

_____

helper(s)

_____

did this activity together

Handy overspill

YOU WILL NEED: a large bowl; a small bowl; a tablespoon and someone to help you.

You are going to measure the volume of your hand!

● Find a bowl large enough for your hand to fit in.

● Place it inside a larger bowl and on a surface where it will not matter if it gets a bit wet!

● Now fill the smaller bowl with water right up to the top.

● Very carefully put your hand into the water. Let the water spill into the larger bowl.

● Very carefully, lift the small bowl out of the larger bowl without spilling any more water then use a tablespoon to measure how much water is in the large bowl. This is a measure of the volume of your hand. Write down the answer.

my bowl held

[ ]

tablespoons

Toy volumes

● Look around your home. Find 5 toys that you like to play with.

● Line them up in order according to the amount of space they would take up in the picnic basket or rucksack if you were going out for the day.

Put the largest one first.

Put the smallest one last.

Put the others in the middle in the correct order.

REMEMBER: you are ordering them according to the amount of space they take up, not according to how tall or short they are!

● Draw them in the right order on a piece of paper or the back of this sheet and ask someone to help you label them.

Dear Parent or Carer

This activity will help your child to understand the concept of volume. The volume of an object is the amount of space that it takes up. Children sometimes judge size purely by how tall or short things are. This is an attempt to get them to think about other aspects of size.

National Curriculum reference: AT 1 and AT 2

_____and

child

_____

helper(s)

_____

did this activity together

Dear Parent or Carer

This activity requires your child to measure the capacity of different containers accurately and using an appropriate unit. Be sure to take care and count the exact number of spoonfuls. Talk about full, half-full and so on.

National Curriculum reference: AT 1 and AT 2

_____and

child

_____

helper(s)

_____

did this activity together

Comparing cups

YOU WILL NEED: a tablespoon; a pencil and water or lentils or rice.

Do you prefer to drink out of a glass, a mug or a cup?

● Choose one thing that you usually drink out of and one thing that your partner usually drinks out of.

● Which one do you think holds the most?

● Now measure how much each of them holds using a tablespoon. How many spoonfuls of water – or lentils or rice – does it take to fill each of them up?

● Draw each mug/cup/glass in the space below and write down the number of spoonfuls it can hold.

impact MATHS HOMEWORK

Value for money?

How do we know how much orange juice or squash there is in a bottle?

Sometimes the shape of a bottle or packet is misleading and it looks bigger than it is – or smaller.

● Choose something that you like to drink.

● Ask your partner if you can go with them to a shop where you can look at different bottles and containers.

● Look at the amount there is in each one, for example in a can, in a bottle, in a packet.

● Write down the different amounts and the prices of each. Use the back of this sheet if your list is too long.

amount	price

Dear Parent or Carer

This activity will lead to a consideration of the different standard units that are used to measure volume – including litres, millilitres, cubic centimetres, pints, quarts, and so on. Please help your child to write down the amount and the unit.

National Curriculum reference: AT 1 and AT 2

_____and

child

_____

helper(s)

_____

did this activity together

_____and

child

_____

helper(s)

_____

did this activity together

Cut it open

YOU WILL NEED: an old box or packet; a pencil and a pair of scissors.

● Look for an old packet or box at home which no-one minds you using. (It is more fun if it is an interesting shape!)

● Look at it carefully. What shapes do you think it would make if you were to cut it open along the edges and lay it out flat?

● Draw the shapes you think it would make.

● Now ask someone to help you cut it open along the edges then lay it out flat.

● What shapes do you see? Draw them.

impact MATHS HOMEWORK

Fold it up

YOU WILL NEED: scissors; card and glue.

You are going to make an unusual box!

● Cut out the shape below. Stick it on to a piece of card (an old birthday or Christmas card will do) and cut round it again.

● Fold it along the dotted lines – and then unfold it and decorate the sides brightly before you fold it up and ask someone to help you stick it together.

● Leave one of the flaps open to make a door!

Dear Parent or Carer

This activity will help to demonstrate we can create a solid shape from a flat 'net'. You will need to give quite a lot of help – especially with the cutting out. Encourage your child to decorate the box nicely before you stick it together.

National Curriculum reference: AT 1 and AT 4

_____and

child

_____

helper(s)

_____

did this activity together

Dear Parent or Carer

This activity will help your child to practise measuring the capacity of a container and gives experience of estimating volume. Discuss how your child may check estimates as accurately as possible.

National Curriculum reference: AT 1 and AT 2

_____and

child

_____

helper(s)

_____

did this activity together

Fair share

YOU WILL NEED: a cup and something dry that pours, such as lentils, dried peas, sugar, salt or rice.

● Fill the cup with lentils.

● Now share its contents into three equal portions. You can do this in any way you like but you must be sure that it is fair!

How can you check?

> HINT: use a tablespoon, or an egg cup, or any small container.

● When you are sure it is fair ask someone to check for you!

● Now can you work out how many tablespoonfuls of lentils fit in your cup. Write down your answer.

my cup held

tablespoonfuls

impact MATHS HOMEWORK

Spilling fun

YOU WILL NEED: two containers of about the same size but not the same shape and a place where it doesn't matter if you make a mess!

● Look at the two containers and discuss with your partner which you think will hold the most.

●Now use water or lentils or rice to fill the one you think is smaller. Make sure it is full to the top!

● Tip the contents into the other container. Were you right – or did some spill over?

● If you were wrong, put a cross by your drawings.

● Draw both containers on a piece of paper or the back of this sheet, and label one large and one small.

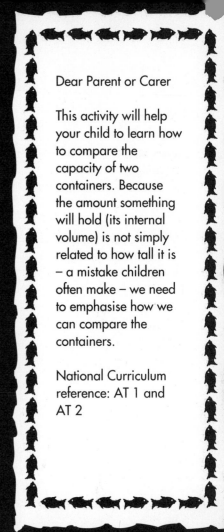

Dear Parent or Carer

This activity will help your child to learn how to compare the capacity of two containers. Because the amount something will hold (its internal volume) is not simply related to how tall it is – a mistake children often make – we need to emphasise how we can compare the containers.

National Curriculum reference: AT 1 and AT 2

_____and

child

_____

helper(s)

_____

did this activity together

Dear Parent or Carer

Although this activity feels like a lot of hard work because you have to find the containers and it can be messy, it really is worth it. Your child will do a great deal of comparing and measuring, and this will develop an understanding of a very difficult concept – that of capacity. Remember the containers can be any shape – mugs, jugs, glasses, shampoo bottles, milk bottles, will all be fine to use!

National Curriculum reference: AT 1 and AT 2

_____and

child

_____

helper(s)

_____

did this activity together

Bubble sort

YOU WILL NEED: several small containers of roughly the same size but different shapes and a place where you can make a bit of a mess!

● Look at your containers. Line them up in order of size with the one that you think contains the most first, down to the one that you think contains the least.

● Draw them in that order on a piece of paper or the back of this sheet.

● Now use water or lentils or rice or salt to fill the one you believe is the largest right up to the top.

impact MATHS HOMEWORK

● Tip its contents gently into the container next to it. Which of the two holds the most? If necessary swap the two containers round so that the largest one is at the end of the line.

● Look at the 2nd and 3rd containers in the line. Fill the 2nd one right up to the top. Tip the contents gently into the 3rd container. Which of these two holds the most? If necessary, swap their places round so that the larger one is 2nd and the smaller is 3rd.

● Keep working like this, comparing containers right down the line until you have them all in order.

This is called a BUBBLE SORT!

● Write 1st, 2nd, 3rd and so on under the appropriate container in your drawing.

_____and

child

_____

helper(s)

_____

did this activity together

Unit hunt

Some things are measured according to their length, others are measured according to their weight, others according to their capacity (how much they hold) and so on.

● Look around your house to find as many different things measured in as many different ways as possible and make a list of them. Remember there may be more than one way of measuring the same thing; for example, weight can be measured in kilograms and grams or in pounds and ounces.

● Make your list as long as you can – writing down the object and the unit it is measured in.

unit	object

impact MATHS HOMEWORK

Are they the same?

● Can you find two things that are roughly the same weight but are different sizes?

● Look at the labels, if they have them. Do they give the weight?

● Draw the objects in the space below and, if there is a label, copy the weight on to your drawing.

Dear Parent or Carer

This activity will help your child realise that things which are the same size can be different weights and things which have the same weight can be different sizes! Talk about how heavy and light things are.

National Curriculum reference: AT 1 and AT 2

_____and

child

_____

helper(s)

_____

did this activity together

_____and

child

_____

helper(s)

_____

did this activity together

Heavy weights

● Look around your home for something which is HEAVIER than you.

● Talk about the thing you find with a grown-up.

● Draw it on a piece of paper or the back of this sheet.

impact MATHS HOMEWORK

Weight watch out

● Ask someone to help you search through your food cupboard for a tin or a packet which contains some food that you like! It must have a weight written on it.

● Draw it carefully on a piece of paper or the back of this sheet.

● How heavy is it? Write down its weight.

It weighs

(REMEMBER to write the unit as well as the number, for example 500g.)

Dear Parent or Carer

This activity introduces the units used for weighing things. We shall be looking at and comparing all types of standard unit, so don't worry which unit is used on your child's drawing.

National Curriculum reference: AT 1 and AT 2

_____and

child

_____

helper(s)

_____

did this activity together

More or less

- Look in your store cupboard. Can you find some tins or packets of food which fit into the following sets:

WEIGHS LESS THAN 500G

WEIGHS MORE THAN 500G AND LESS THAN 1000G

- Find up to five items for each category. Write their names in the chart below.

- Bring one of the labels into school.

WEIGHS LESS THAN 500G	WEIGHS MORE THAN 500G AND LESS THAN 1000G

Dear Parent or Carer

We are working on weight in class and discussing how much different things weigh. This activity will help with estimating and measuring in grams and kilograms.

National Curriculum reference: AT 1 and AT 2

_____and

child

_____

helper(s)

_____

did this activity together

impact MATHS HOMEWORK

Toy weights

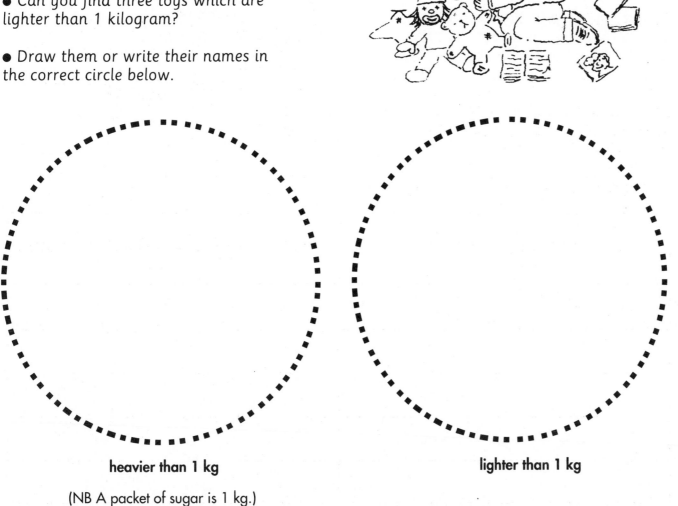

● Look around your house for three toys which are heavier than 1 kilogram.

● Can you find three toys which are lighter than 1 kilogram?

● Draw them or write their names in the correct circle below.

heavier than 1 kg

(NB A packet of sugar is 1 kg.)

lighter than 1 kg

Dear Parent or Carer

This activity will help your child to get a feel for the standard units of weight – kilograms and grams. We will be weighing objects in class and ordering all our toys according to their weight!

National Curriculum reference: AT 1 and AT 2

_____and

child

_____

helper(s)

_____

did this activity together

_____and

child

_____

helper(s)

_____

did this activity together

Wait for the weight

YOU WILL NEED: some small stones or pebbles or beans; a balance or scales; a coin and one counter each.

● Place your counter on the start of the track and take it in turns to spin the coin.

● If it lands heads up move one space forward, if it lands tails up move two spaces.

● Look at the number of the square you land on. You can take that number of stones from the pile.

● When everyone has been round the track and reached the start again, weigh your pebbles.

● The player with the heaviest pile of pebbles is the winner!

impact MATHS HOMEWORK

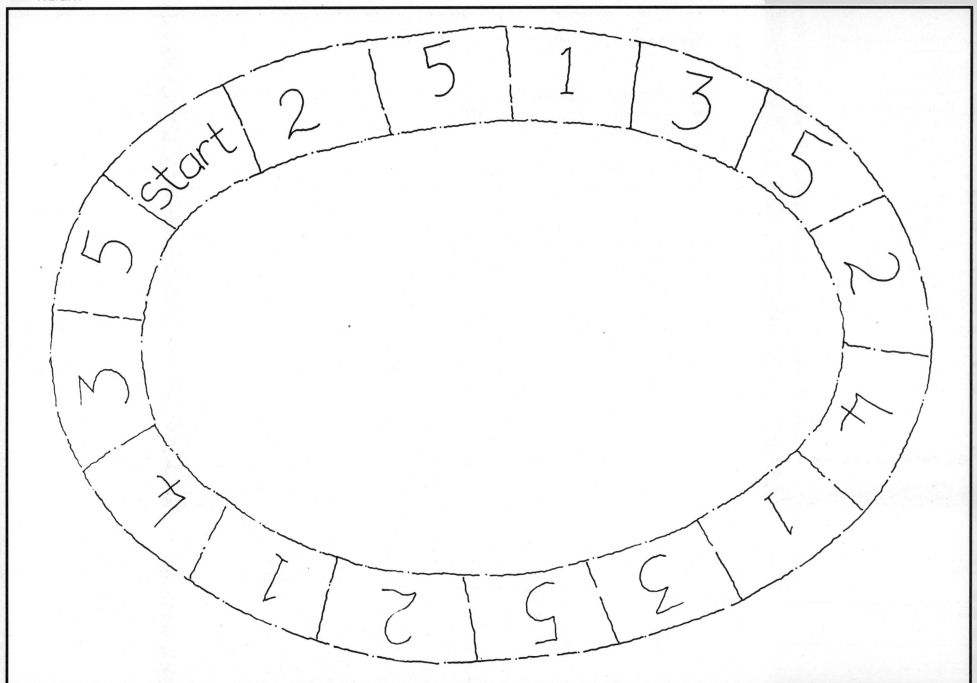

_____and

child

_____

helper(s)

_____

did this activity together

Which coin?

YOU WILL NEED: a handful of change, a small piece of Sellotape or Blu-Tack and a wax crayon or a soft pencil.

● Choose your three favourite coins. (They must all be different.)

● Look at them carefully. What colour are they? What sort of edges do they have – milled (grooved) or smooth? What shape are they?

● Now make a coin rubbing of each one. To do this choose the side with a number on it – if there is one!

● Place the Sellotape (folded) or the Blu-tack on the table and stick the coin on top of it. This helps to keep the coin still.

● Place the paper over the coin. Crayon gently – scribbling across the coin, back and forth, until a picture emerges.

● Do this to all three coins.

impact MATHS HOMEWORK

Coin routes

YOU WILL NEED: a handful of change, a pencil and someone patient to work with!

● Choose a coin and place it at the start of the map below.

● Choose a route for the coin to take, according to the options along the route.

● Do this for several coins. Which shops have no coins in them? Which have lots?

● Write the name of the coins next to the appropriate shops.

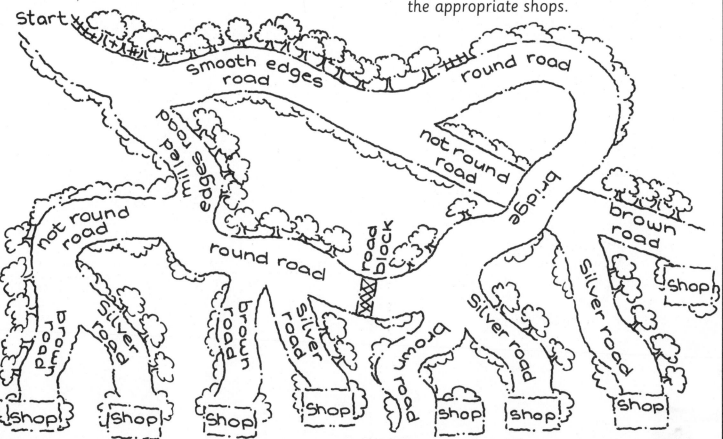

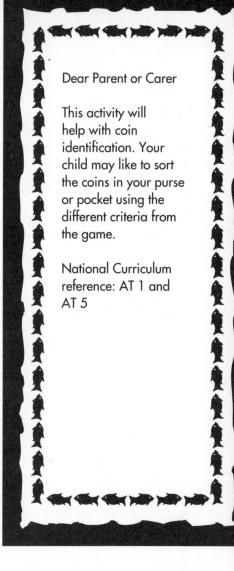

Dear Parent or Carer

This activity will help with coin identification. Your child may like to sort the coins in your purse or pocket using the different criteria from the game.

National Curriculum reference: AT 1 and AT 5

_____and

child

_____

helper(s)

_____

did this activity together

Dear Parent or Carer

This game will help your child to identify the different coins. Please talk about the different values. Your child may like to order the coins from smallest to largest values.

National Curriculum reference: AT 1, AT 2 and AT 5

_____and

child

_____

helper(s)

_____

did this activity together

Collection

YOU WILL NEED: a handful of change, a counter for each player and a dice.

● Put the money in a central pile and your counters on any square of the board to start.

● Take it in turns to throw the dice. Count that number of spaces round (clockwise). When you land on a square take that coin from the pile.

● The first player to collect one of each sort of coin is the winner.

Board squares (clockwise): 1p, 10p, 5p, 20p, 2p, 10p, 5p, 1p, 20p, 2p, 10p, 1p, 5p, 20p, 2p, 10p, 2p, 1p, 5p, 2p, 20p, 2p, 5p, 1p

impact MATHS HOMEWORK

Charting money

YOU WILL NEED: to borrow all the change in someone's purse or pocket!

● Sort the coins into groups according to their value and place the coins in piles in the correct circles on this page.

● Now count how many there are of each type of coin. What is the total value of each pile? Write in the amounts.

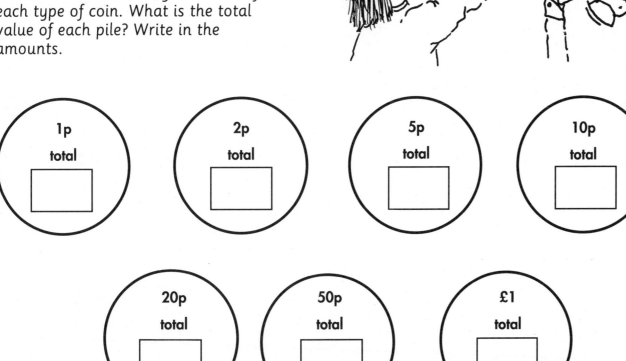

1p
total

2p
total

5p
total

10p
total

20p
total

50p
total

£1
total

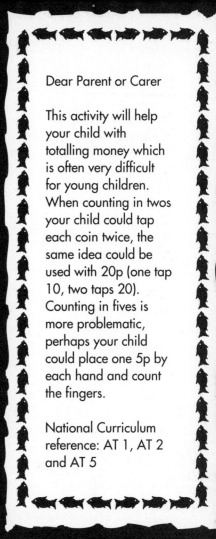

Dear Parent or Carer

This activity will help your child with totalling money which is often very difficult for young children. When counting in twos your child could tap each coin twice, the same idea could be used with 20p (one tap 10, two taps 20). Counting in fives is more problematic, perhaps your child could place one 5p by each hand and count the fingers.

National Curriculum reference: AT 1, AT 2 and AT 5

_____and
child

_____
helper(s)

_____

did this activity together

_____and

child

_____

helper(s)

_____

did this activity together

Venn money

YOU WILL NEED: a handful of change and a pencil.

● Sort the change on to the Venn diagram below. Make sure that any coin that belongs inside both circles goes in the overlap section, and any coin which does not fit in either, goes outside both.

● Draw round each coin you have placed on the diagram and label it.

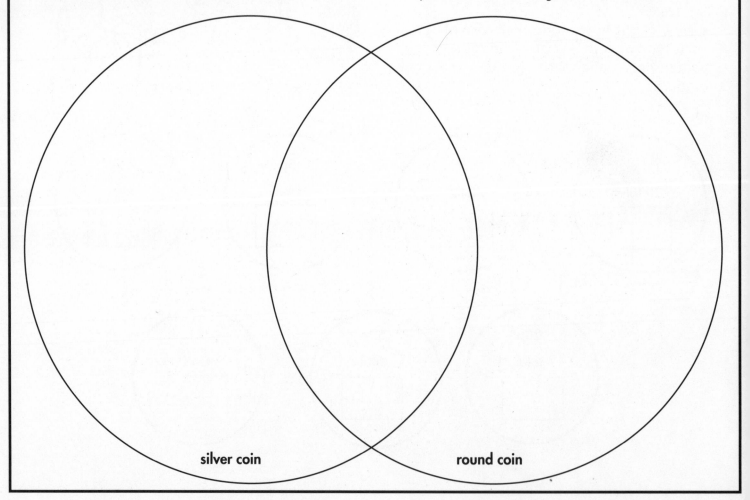

silver coin   round coin

impact MATHS HOMEWORK

Window shopping

Window shopping is when you go out to the shops and look but you don't actually buy anything!

● Go window shopping with someone. Have a look and see what you would like to buy.

● Choose one thing – it must cost less than £5.

● When you get home, draw it. Write the price beside it.

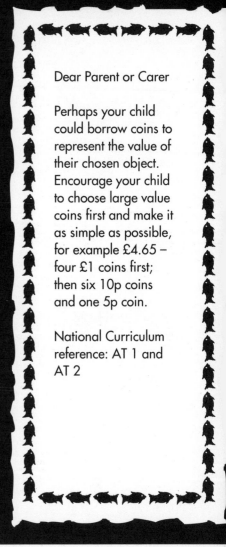

Dear Parent or Carer

Perhaps your child could borrow coins to represent the value of their chosen object. Encourage your child to choose large value coins first and make it as simple as possible, for example £4.65 – four £1 coins first; then six 10p coins and one 5p coin.

National Curriculum reference: AT 1 and AT 2

_____and

child

_____

helper(s)

_____

did this activity together

Big money

● Ask someone if they will let you look at their money. You need to look at as many notes as you can – preferably at a £5 note and a £10 note, and possibly at a £20 note!

● Study the notes carefully. Can you see any differences?

● Draw one of the notes below. Can you draw the number of £1 coins it is worth?

_____and

child

_____

helper(s)

_____

did this activity together

Coin toss up

YOU WILL NEED: a handful of coins.

● Put the money in a central pile.

● Take it in turns to choose 4 coins and toss them (gently) into the air.

● Any of them which land heads you may keep.

● Keep playing until there is no money left in the central pile.

● Add up how much you have. The person with the most money is the winner!

Dear Parent or Carer

Help your child to arrange the coins in order from largest to smallest value. This will help with totalling.

National Curriculum reference: AT 1 and AT 2

_____and

child

_____

helper(s)

_____

did this activity together

_____and

child

_____

helper(s)

_____

did this activity together

Handy coins

YOU WILL NEED: a pencil and paper and a handful of coins.

● Place the coins in a central pile.

● Each player must draw round their hand with the fingers outstretched.

● Now take it in turns to choose a coin from the pile. Place the coin on a fingertip on the drawing of your hand.

● Continue playing until every finger on the drawing is covered.

● Add up how much money you have on your hand. The player with the most is the winner.

● Draw round the coins on your hands and label them.

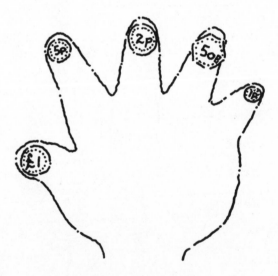

impact MATHS HOMEWORK

Price tags

On this page are pictures of things that most families buy each week.

● Look at them all. Guess how much each thing costs. Write your guess in the chart below.

● Now ask someone to help you find the correct prices. Write them down.

How close were you?

item	guess	price
bread		
margarine		
apple		
orange		
milk		
tea		
jam		
eggs		
potatoes		
cheese		

Dear Parent or Carer

Estimating prices will be difficult for your child, perhaps you could guess together. Allow your child to use real money for this activity.

National Curriculum reference: AT 2

_____and

child

_____

helper(s)

_____

did this activity together

_____and

child

.

_____

helper(s)

did this activity together

Buy a dinosaur

YOU WILL NEED: a dice, a handful of coins and some crayons.

● Place the coins in a central pile.

● Take it in turns to throw the dice. Collect the amount of money (in pence) shown by the number of dots on the dice.

● When you have collected enough money, you can buy a piece of your dinosaur.

● Put the money back on the pile and colour the dinosaur piece in to show that you have paid for it.

● Now continue playing. The first person to pay for and colour their whole dinosaur is the winner!

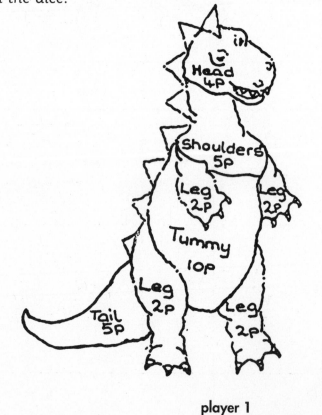

player 1

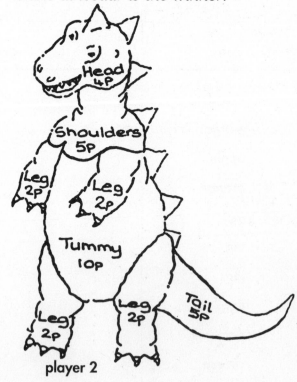

player 2

Safe purses

YOU WILL NEED: a dice, a lot of 1p coins, some 5p coins and three 10p coins.

● Take it in turns to throw the dice. Collect the number thrown in 1p coins.

● Place them on your 'hand' in the chart on the right. If you have five coins on your 'hand', you may swap them for a 5p coin which you place in your 'purse'.

● Keep playing until you have two 5p coins in your 'purse'. You may swap these for a 10p coin which you place in your 'safe'.

● The first player to get two 10p coins in their safe is the winner! Good luck!

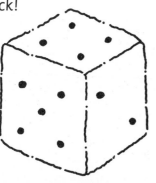

player 1	player 2
Safe	Safe
Purse	Purse
Hand	Hand

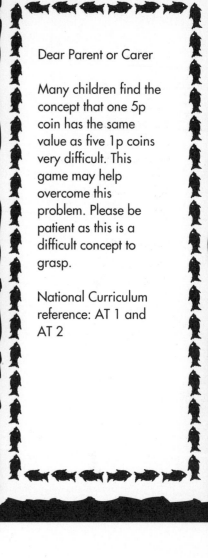

Dear Parent or Carer

Many children find the concept that one 5p coin has the same value as five 1p coins very difficult. This game may help overcome this problem. Please be patient as this is a difficult concept to grasp.

National Curriculum reference: AT 1 and AT 2

_____and

child

_____

helper(s)

_____

did this activity together

Dear Parent or Carer

Allow your child to use real money and give plenty of time to experiment with different value coins. Encourage your child to be systematic when recording the results.

National Curriculum reference: AT 1 and AT 2

_____and

child

_____

helper(s)

_____

did this activity together

Coin thief

YOU WILL NEED: a helper with lots of imagination!

● Imagine that a coin thief has stolen all the 1p coins in Britain! Which amounts of money will we be unable to make?

● Using our other coins, try out all the amounts between 0p and £1. What prices would be possible? Which would be impossible?

● When you have worked them out write them in the squares below.

What about giving change?

● Talk to your helper about why we need a 1p coin!

impact MATHS HOMEWORK

Nine pence change

YOU WILL NEED: a handful of 10p and 20p coins, a dice.

● Place the coins in a central pile.

● Take it in turns to throw the dice. Look at the number thrown and take that number of coins – either 10ps or 20ps or a mixture from the pile.

● Add them together.

You are trying to buy one of the items pictured below BUT you can only buy one if you need 9p change or less.

● If you can buy one colour it in to show that you have bought it and place the coins back on the pile. If you can't buy one, keep one coin and put the rest back.

● Keep playing until all the objects have been bought. The player who has bought the most items is the winner.

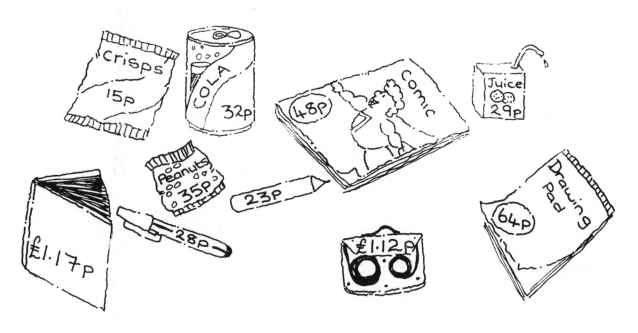

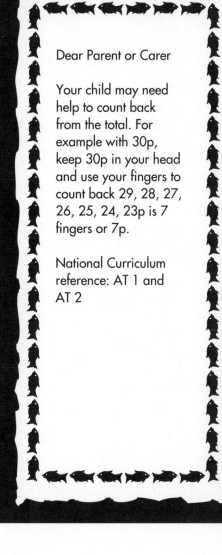

Dear Parent or Carer

Your child may need help to count back from the total. For example with 30p, keep 30p in your head and use your fingers to count back 29, 28, 27, 26, 25, 24, 23p is 7 fingers or 7p.

National Curriculum reference: AT 1 and AT 2

_____and

child

_____

helper(s)

_____

did this activity together

Dinosaur change

YOU WILL NEED: a handful of coins;
a dice; a counter for each player and
the dinosaur on the accompanying sheet.

● Each take 20p in change and place the
rest of the coins in a central pile.

● To start, place your counters on the
dinosaur's tail.

● Take it in turns to throw the dice and
move that number of spaces along the
dinosaur, moving to any adjacent
patch.

If you land on an amount of
money, you must pay that
amount to the central pile. (You
will need to collect your change.)

If you land on a shaded patch you
may take a 10p coin from the pile.

● Keep playing until you have both
reached the head of the dinosaur. The
player with the amount nearest to 10p
is the winner!

Dear Parent or Carer

Help your child to
make change, for
example if your child
has a 5p and the
patch costs 3p then
remember 3p and
count on 4p, 5p using
1p coins. This leaves
2p change.

National Curriculum
reference: AT 1 and
AT 2

_____and
child

_____
helper(s)

....

did this activity together

impact MATHS HOMEWORK

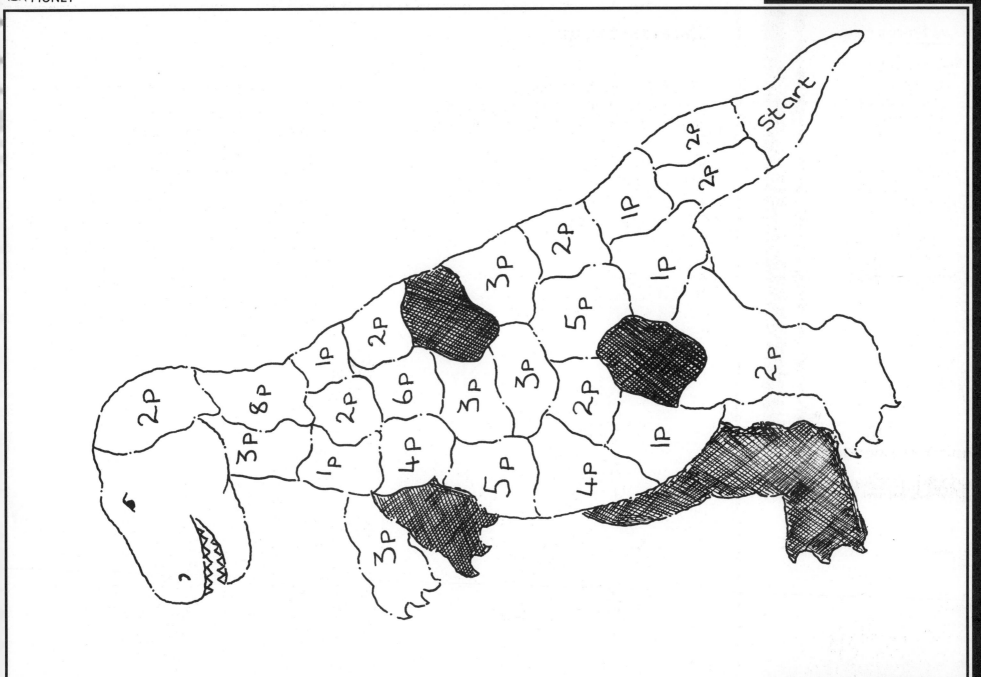

_____and

child

_____

helper(s)

_____

did this activity together

Lose it

YOU WILL NEED: a handful of coins for each player (about the same amount if possible) and a dice.

● Take it in turns to throw the dice.

● Give your partner the amount shown by the dice, in money. So if you throw a 5, you give them 5p. Use whichever coins you like. You may have to give one another change.

● Keep on playing. The first player to get rid of all their money is the winner.

● If the game goes on a long time, you can stop playing and add up your money to see who has the least!

impact MATHS HOMEWORK

Buying five

price

● Ask someone to tell you the price of something you like to eat for a treat!

It might be a chocolate bar, a packet of crisps, some nuts or raisins, a fizzy drink ...

● If possible, find a label or packet from your treat.

● Draw the label in the space above and write down the price next to it.

● Can you work out how much it would cost to buy five of these items?

> (HINT: you could try working out how much ten cost)

Dear Parent or Carer

Encourage your child to use real money to place by their label and consider different ways of making up the value.

National Curriculum reference: AT 1 and AT 2

_____and

child

_____

helper(s)

_____

did this activity together

_____and

child

_____

helper(s)

_____

did this activity together

Coin animal

YOU WILL NEED: a handful of coins, a pencil and some crayons or felt-tipped pens.

You are going to draw a coin animal!

● Lay your coins out in the shape of an animal in the space below.

● Now draw round each coin.

● Write the number of the coin on its outline.

● Colour in your animal and add eyes, ears, a tail and whiskers or whatever else it needs!

impact MATHS HOMEWORK

My favourite day

- Choose your favourite day and colour in its name.

- Draw a picture in the middle of the circle to show why it is your favourite.

Monday

Tuesday

Wednesday

Thursday

Friday

Saturday

Sunday

Dear Parent or Carer

Help your child to learn the days of the week in sequence. Talk about favourite days, for example visiting Granny on Sunday, swimming on Thursday.

National Curriculum reference: AT 1 and AT 2

_____and

child

_____

helper(s)

_____

did this activity together

_____and

child

_____

helper(s)

_____

did this activity together

Day and night

Are the things people do in the daytime and at night different?

Draw two daytime activities.

Draw two nighttime activities.

impact MATHS HOMEWORK

Today, tomorrow, yesterday

● Choose a day and fill in the spaces.

Today is

_____ day

I am

_____

Yesterday I was

_____

Tomorrow will be

_____ day.

I shall be

_____

Draw a picture of something you did yesterday.

Dear Parent or Carer

These words and the tenses used are very difficult for children to understand.
Talk about what happened yesterday. Your child can then draw the most exciting memory from yesterday. We anticipate the future when we talk about tomorrow, using phrases like: We will be ...

National Curriculum reference: AT 1 and AT 2

_____ and

child

_____

helper(s)

_____

did this activity together

_____and

child

_____

helper(s)

_____

did this activity together

What shall I wear?

● Draw a picture of yourself wearing the clothes that would be suitable for each season.

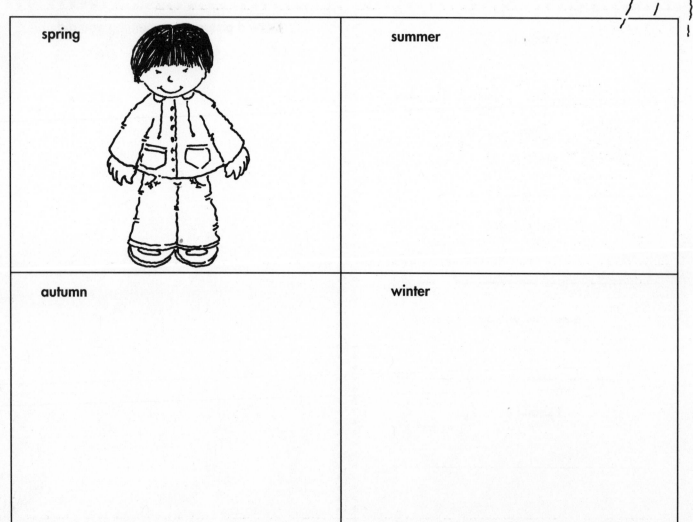

spring	summer
autumn	winter

impact MATHS HOMEWORK

The apple tree

● Draw how you think the apple tree will look in different seasons.

WINTER	SPRING
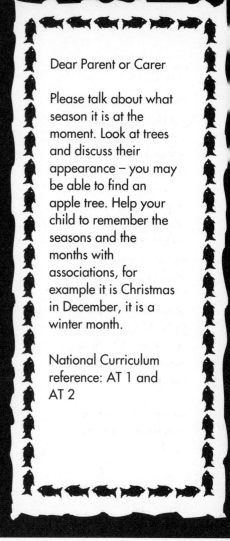	
AUTUMN	SUMMER

Dear Parent or Carer

Please talk about what season it is at the moment. Look at trees and discuss their appearance – you may be able to find an apple tree. Help your child to remember the seasons and the months with associations, for example it is Christmas in December, it is a winter month.

National Curriculum reference: AT 1 and AT 2

_____and

child

_____

helper(s)

_____

did this activity together

Breakfast time

How long does it take to eat your breakfast?

● Write in the rest of the numbers on the clock faces before you start this activity then draw in the hands to show the following times.

I started to eat my breakfast at:

I finished eating my breakfast at:

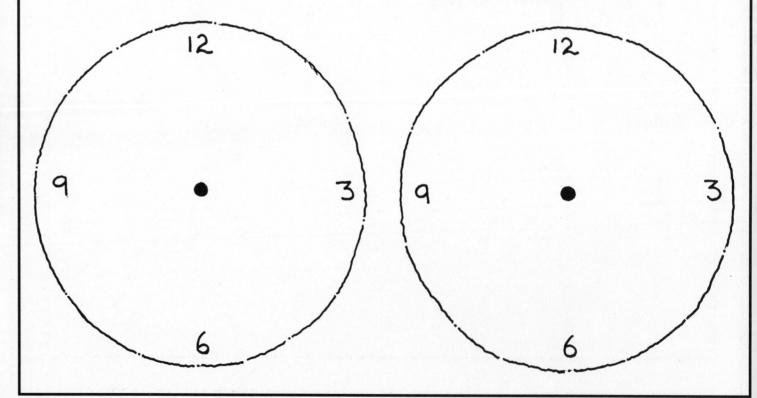

impact MATHS HOMEWORK

Measuring time

● Draw pictures of everything you can find at home that measures the time.

Dear Parent or Carer

Talk to your child about the different clocks on heating systems, videos, cookers, etc. Discuss their different functions. Some may be 24 hour clocks, some may have a digital display, some may show seconds.

National Curriculum reference: AT 1 and AT 2

_____and

child

_____

helper(s)

_____

did this activity together

Roman numbers

● Can you find a clock or watch with Roman numbers?

● Put the numbers on to this clock face.

● Can you find out how the numbers work?

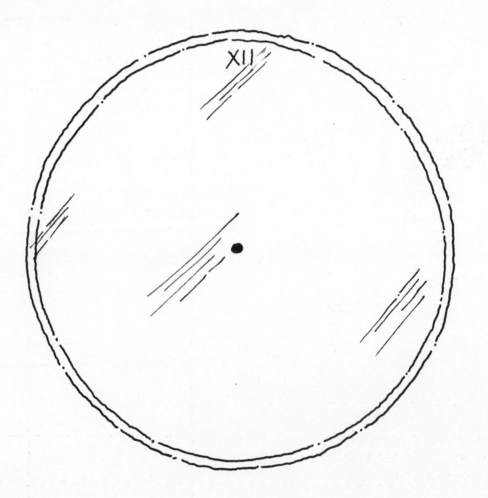

_____and

child

_____

helper(s)

_____

did this activity together

impact MATHS HOMEWORK

Pace it out

YOU WILL NEED: a pencil and a watch with a second hand.

How many paces can you take in 30 seconds?

30 seconds is half a minute.

● Mark your starting position then count your paces for 30 seconds. (Ask your partner to time you.)

● Ask other members of your family to try. Record their results in the chart below.

● Predict how many paces you could take in one minute.

family member	number of paces

Dear Parent or Carer

Children enjoy competition. This will help them to time 30 seconds and record their work. Please give help with recording the results.

National Curriculum reference: AT 1 and AT 2

_____and

child

_____

helper(s)

_____

did this activity together

Dear Parent or Carer

Telling the time is very difficult for many children. Telling the difference between the hour and minute hand and realising that the minutes are counted by the small demarcations will help. Discuss the passing of minutes whenever possible, for example, mark the minute hand position before sharing a book then count the minutes that have passed.

National Curriculum reference: AT 1 and AT 2

_____and

child

_____

helper(s)

_____

did this activity together

My favourite television programme

● Do you have a favourite television programme? Write in the information below. (You may need to look at a newspaper.)

My favourite television programme is

and it is on a

day.

My favourite television programme begins

at [ ] **o'clock and ends**

at [ ] **o'clock.**

● Draw in the times below:

My programme lasted

[ ] **minutes.**

impact MATHS HOMEWORK

Years go by

What has happened in your family since 1980?

What will happen in the next few years?

● Write down any important event that happened or will happen in the correct year on the time track.

1980
1981
1982
1983
1984
1985
1986
1987
1988
1989
1990
1991
1992
1993
1994
1995
1996
1997
1998
1999
2000

Dear Parent or Carer

Talk to your child about this year. What age are the members of your family this year? These can be entered on the time-line. How old will your family be in the year 2000? Fill in significant family events. Please talk about events before your child was born, family photographs are fun and a good way to show how things change.

National Curriculum reference: AT 1 and AT 2

_____and

child

_____

helper(s)

_____

did this activity together

_____and

child

_____

helper(s)

_____

did this activity together

My family history

● Write the names of all the children in your family on the bottom shelf.

● Now can you find out the correct names to write on the higher shelves?

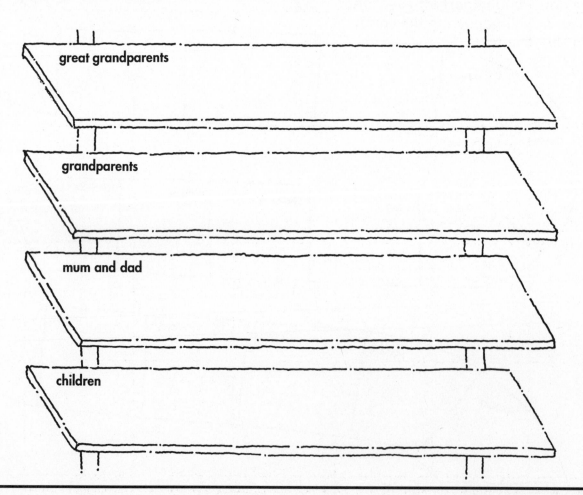

great grandparents

grandparents

mum and dad

children

impact MATHS HOMEWORK

Moon watch

● For this activity you will need to watch the moon every night for one month. Each night you see the moon draw its shape and note the date. If it is a cloudy night you might like to guess the moon's shape.

Dear Parent or Carer

Children are fascinated by the moon. Try to find a suitable time to observe the apparent change in the moon's shape. You may like to cut out pictures from the newspaper and match these with your observations.

National Curriculum reference: AT 1 and AT 2

_____and

child

_____

helper(s)

_____

did this activity together

Dear Parent or Carer

Children find telling the time difficult. It helps if they are able to associate different times with particular events, for example bedtime or time to leave for school. Talk about reading a digital clock. Your child should also look at an analogue clock face and be encouraged to say it is 35 minutes PAST 6 (do not talk about 'to the next hour' yet).

National Curriculum reference: AT 1 and AT 2

_____and

child

_____

helper(s)

_____

did this activity together

Digital/analogue

- Look at a digital and an analogue clock at the same time.

- Record the time on the clocks below.

- What would you or your family normally be doing at this time?

- Now choose a time when your family will be doing something special. Record this time on the other two clocks.

- Draw the two activities on a piece of paper or the back of this sheet.

impact MATHS HOMEWORK

In the wash

YOU WILL NEED: a watch and a pencil.

● Ask if you can watch the next time the washing machine is used in your house.

● Record the time that the machine started and when the machine finished on the clocks below.

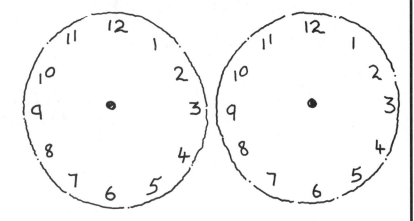

● Does the cycle take more than 60 minutes (1 hour)? Tick the correct box.

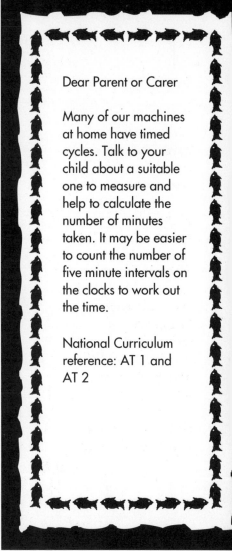

Dear Parent or Carer

Many of our machines at home have timed cycles. Talk to your child about a suitable one to measure and help to calculate the number of minutes taken. It may be easier to count the number of five minute intervals on the clocks to work out the time.

National Curriculum reference: AT 1 and AT 2

_____ and
child

_____
helper(s)

_____

did this activity together

Dear Parent or Carer

Please help your child to draw in the times before and after each meal. Count the minutes between the two. Discuss how little the hour hand has moved.

National Curriculum reference: AT 1 and AT 2

_____and

child

_____

helper(s)

_____

did this activity together

Eating times

● Look at the time before you begin each meal and again at the end. Draw the time on the clocks. (Pay attention to the position of the minute hand.)

● Now count the minutes between the two times and write them in below. Did you spend more than 60 minutes (1 hour) eating today?

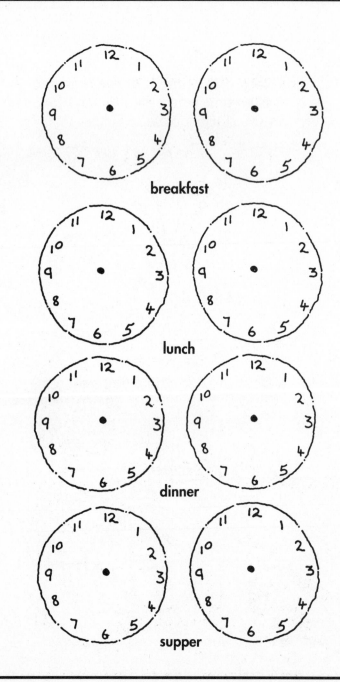

breakfast

lunch

dinner

supper

Breakfast _____ minutes	
Lunch _____ minutes	
Dinner _____ minutes	
Supper _____ minutes	
[ ]	minutes altogether

impact MATHS HOMEWORK

Hop along

YOU WILL NEED: a stopwatch or clock which can time seconds and minutes.

> **How long does it take to hop a hundred paces?**

● Go to the park with your family. (Remember to take something that can be used to time the activity.)

● Ask your partner to help you mark out 100 paces.

● How long does it take you to hop this distance?

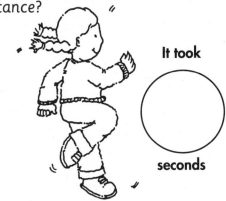

It took

seconds

● Now try skipping or bunny hopping.

● Design a chart on a piece of paper or the back of this sheet to show your results.

Dear Parent or Carer

You may need to help your child to design a chart and to record the times.
This activity will give you plenty of opportunity to talk about vocabulary such as fastest, slowest, and so on.

National Curriculum reference: AT 1 and AT 2

_____and

child

_____

helper(s)

_____

did this activity together

Travelling to work

Dear Parent or Carer

You will need to help your child to count in five minute intervals from the departure to the arrival time. Draw clocks by drawing round small circular objects (cups) and putting the numbers on. (Begin with the quarter numbers, i.e. 12, 6, 3, 9.) Discuss whether the longest journey takes the longest time.

National Curriculum reference: AT 1 and AT 2

- Ask members of your family how long it takes them to get to work. What time do they leave and what time do they arrive?

- How many minutes does it take each person to travel to work? Write all the names and times in order in the chart below.

name	time they leave	time they arrive

- Draw a clock to show when the journey began and another clock to show when the journey ended. Do this for everyone in your family.

_____and

child

_____

helper(s)

_____

did this activity together

impact MATHS HOMEWORK

24 hours in the day

The hands of a clock go round twice in one day – 24 hours.

● Ask your partner to help you to write or draw 3 things that happen in your family at important times during the 24 hours in the boxes. Draw in the times on the clocks.

● What will be the time on a 24 hour clock?

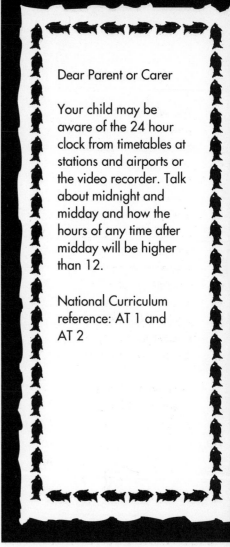

Dear Parent or Carer

Your child may be aware of the 24 hour clock from timetables at stations and airports or the video recorder. Talk about midnight and midday and how the hours of any time after midday will be higher than 12.

National Curriculum reference: AT 1 and AT 2

_____and

child

_____

helper(s)

_____

did this activity together

_____and

child

_____

helper(s)

_____

did this activity together

Just a minute

● What can you do in 1 minute?

● Make a chart to represent the results. How many times can you write 'said' in 1 minute? Try hopping up and down or counting. How many times can you hop? How far can you count?
Ask other members of your family to try.

family member	things done in 1 minute	number of times

impact MATHS HOMEWORK